Old Master Drawings
from Chatsworth

91. REMBRANDT VAN RIJN: David's Charge to Solomon

Old Master Drawings from Chatsworth

A LOAN EXHIBITION

FROM THE DEVONSHIRE COLLECTION

INTRODUCTION AND CATALOGUE BY JAMES BYAM SHAW

FOREWORD BY THOMAS S. WRAGG

CIRCULATED BY THE

International Exhibitions Foundation

1969–1970

Participating Museums

NATIONAL GALLERY OF ART
WASHINGTON · D.C.

PHILADELPHIA MUSEUM OF ART
PHILADELPHIA · PENNSYLVANIA

THE PIERPONT MORGAN LIBRARY
NEW YORK · NEW YORK

ART GALLERY OF ONTARIO
TORONTO · CANADA

ART INSTITUTE OF CHICAGO
CHICAGO · ILLINOIS

LOS ANGELES COUNTY MUSEUM OF ART
LOS ANGELES · CALIFORNIA

M. H. DE YOUNG MEMORIAL MUSEUM
SAN FRANCISCO · CALIFORNIA

WILLIAM ROCKHILL NELSON GALLERY OF ART
KANSAS CITY · MISSOURI

MUSEUM OF ART · RHODE ISLAND SCHOOL OF DESIGN
PROVIDENCE · RHODE ISLAND

THE MUSEUM OF FINE ARTS
HOUSTON · TEXAS

LIBRARY OF CONGRESS CATALOG CARD NO. 74-97171
PRODUCED BY THE MERIDEN GRAVURE COMPANY AND THE STINEHOUR PRESS

COVER ILLUSTRATION: Cat. No. 49. Il Parmigianino, *The Virgin and Child*

Acknowledgments

IT IS with profound pleasure that I write these few remarks as an introduction to the catalogue of the exhibition, "Old Master Drawings from Chatsworth." This is the third exhibition of drawings from the Collection of the Dukes of Devonshire that I have been privileged to organize for leading museums in the United States and Canada. It follows the showing of "Old Master Drawings" in 1962–1963, and "Festival Designs by Inigo Jones" in 1967–1968.

In the course of many visits to Chatsworth, I have been impressed by the unique beauty and extraordinary quality of the drawings, as well as by the warm hospitality accorded me during the course of more than ten years.

While the aesthetic enjoyment of these masterpieces is undisputed, there are other important reasons for their presentation to a large and ever-widening circle of scholars, collectors, university professors and students, notably, the chance to conduct research in the presence of the originals and to weigh complicated attributions. In this respect, the catalogue should prove to be of great value, for like its two predecessors, it contains concise information and fine illustrations not available heretofore.

It is always difficult to thank adequately those who lend treasures from their collections for extended periods. Their Graces, the Duke and Duchess of Devonshire, and the Trustees of the Chatsworth Settlement, deserve our deepest gratitude for so generous a loan. We also wish to express our thanks to Mr. Thomas S. Wragg, Librarian and Keeper at Chatsworth, and an old friend, who has worked with us for many years on this project. Mr. James Byam Shaw, eminent scholar and writer, has contributed the Introduction and individual descriptions to this catalogue, a task which involved much research. He has placed us deeply in his debt.

We wish to thank His Excellency, John Freeman, British Ambassador to the United States, for his willingness to sponsor the exhibition during its tour, and Sir Edward Tomkins, Minister, for assisting us in many ways.

Among the many friends who have made this exhibition possible, we should like to single out Mr. Harold Hugo, Director of the Meriden Gravure Company, who personally visited Chatsworth to acquaint himself with the Collection; Mrs. Leslie Judd Ahlander, who assisted with editorial tasks; and Mr. Kurt Wiener, who advised us on many details of this catalogue. The directors and curators of the participating museums also deserve our thanks, since it is only through their whole-hearted cooperation that these increasingly complex tours are made possible.

ANNEMARIE H. POPE
President
International Exhibitions Foundation

Foreword

MANY who read this will remember the previous exhibition of 114 drawings from Chatsworth which was seen in America and Canada in 1962–63 and has this year been shown in London at the Royal Academy. In my introduction to the catalogue of this exhibition I wrote on the history of the collection at some length and those who would like more information than it is possible to include in this short note should refer to this.

Considered as a whole the splendid collection of drawings by old masters, acquired mainly by the 2nd Duke, son of the builder of the present house, is today the most precious possession among the many treasures of Chatsworth, the Derbyshire home of the Dukes of Devonshire. Many of the works of art there today were until comparatively recent years at other great houses, including Devonshire House, Piccadilly and Chiswick Villa, then the property of the family, but the drawings have been at Chatsworth since their purchase in the first half of the eighteenth century, although until the 6th Duke's Theatre was converted into an exhibition gallery in 1963 it was not possible to display any considerable selection from them for the pleasure of the many visitors to the house.

The present Palladian house at Chatsworth was built by William Cavendish, 4th Earl, and later 1st Duke of Devonshire, in the years between 1687 and 1707, to replace the Elizabethan house which occupied the same site. His son, the 2nd Duke of Devonshire who inherited this new house on his father's death in 1707, was one of the great collectors of his day. Today his collection of drawings survives practically intact as a memorial to his taste. It is likely that it was he, rather than his father, who was responsible for purchases at the Lely and Lankrink Sales in the late seventeenth century, but his greatest acquisitions were made from 1723 onwards. In that year he acquired a large group of splendid drawings from the collection of Nicolaes Anthoni Flinck of Rotterdam, son of Govaert Flinck, a pupil of Rembrandt. He is thought to have bought these "unseen," but there is a possibility that he had seen this collection and others, as a young man when he saw service in the Netherlands. (From this source came the incomparable series of Rembrandt landscapes and most of the large group of drawings by Rubens and Van Dyck.) According to contemporary accounts the Flinck collection consisted of some 500 drawings, but there are only 225 drawings bearing his mark at Chatsworth —of these only 105 have the 2nd Duke's mark in addition and it has been suggested that the remainder may have been acquired later, by the 3rd Duke. There is nothing conclusive about this, however, as it would appear that the 3rd Duke continued to use his father's mark, while a considerable number of drawings acquired by the 2nd Duke himself do not bear it. In fact it is to be found on only 550 drawings (about a third of the whole collection). In a letter preserved at Chatsworth the French connoisseur, Crozat, writing to congratulate the Duke on his purchase, says: "I take the liberty of complimenting you on the drawings of Mr. Flinck of Rotterdam which you have just acquired. It is in my opinion the finest and best chosen collection I have ever seen and will materially enrich yours and make you the richest nobleman in Europe. All the drawings are admirable and worthy to find a place in your collection. I know the selection you had already made was no less choice." A more recent appraisal of the collection as a whole is to be found in Mr. Popham's Introduction to the Exhibition organised by the Arts Council in 1949, where he said: "The contents of the collection as a whole provide a well-balanced illustration of the art of drawing in Europe from the time of the Renaissance to the end of the seventeenth century. There is no great period or phase of art, hardly a great name, except Michelangelo's, which is not represented. The Italian quattrocento, the High Renaissance, with its magnificent Raphaels and its extraordinarily rich representation of Raphael's school, Dürer and Holbein in Germany, Rubens and above all Van Dyck and Rembrandt in the Netherlands . . . the mannerist and baroque painters of Italy, all are here."

The following details of the numbers of drawings in the larger groups by important artists will give a better idea of the resources of the collection—of Italian artists, there are 30 drawings attributed to Raphael, 40 by Giulio Romano, more than 70 by Parmigianino, 30 attributed to Peruzzi, over 80 by the Carraccii, 30 Guercinos (including the fine series of 20 landscapes of which 14 were engraved by J. Pesne) and a group of 30 drawings by Campagnola. Of Northern artists, Rembrandt accounts for 36 drawings (including the splendid group of 29 landscapes), and as one would expect Van Dyck and Rubens have strong representation, with 40 and 30 subjects respectively, while despite the loss of the Liber Veritatis (handed over to the nation in 1957) there are still 20 drawings by Claude at Chatsworth. In addition to 5 drawings in the mounted series, Callot is strongly represented by the drawings in the now celebrated Callot Album, which in addition to 140 drawings, contains 270 prints by the artist. The history of this volume is described by Mr. Byam Shaw in his catalogue note under this artist. Although the volume itself was exhibited at the French Landscape Exhibition at the Royal Academy in 1949, the present exhibition is the first occasion on which it has been feasible to show a group of drawings from it, these having been temporarily removed for the occasion.

Eventually, the 2nd Duke's collection was supplemented by the great collections of Richard Boyle, 3rd Earl of Burlington, through the marriage of Boyle's daughter and eventual heiress, Charlotte, to the Marquess of Hartington, later 4th Duke of Devonshire, in 1748. His architectural drawings have, since 1894, been on permanent loan to the Royal Institute of British Architects, but the important series of drawings for the Court Masques by Inigo Jones, a selection of which was exhibited in America in 1967–68 and has this year been seen in London and Venice, is still at Chatsworth. The Inigo Jones designs were fully catalogued by Simpson and Bell in Volume XII of the Walpole Society's publications, but the catalogue of the Old Master Drawings exists in typescript only. Since the 1962 Exhibition, however, the whole collection has been photographed by the Courtauld Institute of Art, London, and, as an index to the photographs a short-title catalogue, arranged alphabetically by schools, has been compiled and is available to galleries and other institutions.

In addition to the ready access granted to properly accredited students to the collections at Chatsworth, the Duke of Devonshire and the Chatsworth Trustees lend generously. From the drawings alone, this year, in addition to the present exhibition, the exhibition which toured America in 1962–63 has been shown at the Royal Academy. Also the large group of drawings by Inigo Jones, exhibited as "Festival Designs" in America in 1967–68 has been lent to the Victoria & Albert Museum and later to the Giorgio Cini Foundation in Venice. In addition a sizable group of Rembrandt landscapes is included in the Tercentenary Exhibition in Amsterdam, while smaller groups of drawings will have been lent to several major exhibitions in various countries.

THOMAS S. WRAGG

Introduction

SOME of the great private collections of drawings in England, that prompted Richardson to describe that country as the "Cabinet des Desseins" of the world, have been dispersed; and many have come into existence there, and been broken up, since Richardson wrote. That of Sir Thomas Lawrence, for example, whose stamp is a hall-mark of quality, and much more recently those of J. P. Heseltine and Henry Oppenheimer, have made their contribution to the treasures of the museums and private collections of America. But as Mr. Popham suggested, in his introduction to the Arts Council Exhibition of Chatsworth drawings in London twenty years ago, Richardson, when he wrote those words in 1728, was thinking above all of the collection formed over the previous forty years or so by the second Duke of Devonshire; which had been lately crowned, in 1723, by the acquisition of about five hundred drawings, Italian as well as Dutch and Flemish, from the collection of Nicholas Flinck, the son of a pupil of Rembrandt. I say "over the previous forty years," for it seems almost certain that the Duke, before he succeeded to that title, had been an eager bidder at the sale of the collection of Sir Peter Lely in 1688, when he was only twenty-three years old (see the note to No. 59 of this catalogue). The collection then formed is still intact to this day; but though successive Dukes of Devonshire and the Chatsworth Trustees have been most generous in lending individual drawings to the great exhibitions, at the Royal Academy and elsewhere, in the present century, and in allowing visiting scholars to pursue their studies in the great house, comparatively few of these have examined the collection as a whole. The house, in the beautiful countryside of the Peak district of Derbyshire, is remote; the drawings, in the interests of conservation, are no longer on permanent display there; and to the thousands of tourists who make the journey from the nearest cities on the open days, Chatsworth has many other treasures to show. The fame of the collection of drawings, therefore, has something legendary about it.

It is not my part to give an account, even briefly, of its history. It would be interesting to explore further the activities of the second Duke as a collector; to search the surviving marked catalogues of sales, at which in his time the nobility and gentry frequently appeared in person; to see how his aims and achievements in this field coincided or conflicted with those of his competitors—such as his younger contemporary and fellow-soldier, John Guise, whose collection also remains intact at Christ Church, Oxford, and who, like the Duke, acquired so many of his drawings from the collections of Sir Peter Lely and of John, Lord Somers. They must surely have fished in the same streams; and it may be that both derived inspiration from the enthusiasms of Dean Aldrich of Christ Church, to whom some two thousand drawings collected by the celebrated Padre Sebastiano Resta, and afterwards bought by Lord Somers, were described (and apparently offered for about £500) early in 1710 by the architect, John Talman. But the history has been touched upon with better authority by Mr. Popham, and by successive Librarians of Chatsworth, Mr. Arthur Strong, Mr. Francis Thompson and Mr. Thomas Wragg, in various publications in the past; and Mr. Wragg, the present Librarian and Keeper, gives the outline of it here.

There have been since the last war three general exhibitions of selected drawings from Chatsworth: one at the Arts Council house in St. James's Square, London, in 1949, one at the Manchester City Art Gallery in 1961, and the circulating exhibition organized by Mrs. John Pope for the Smithsonian Institution, which was seen at seven of the principal museums of North America in 1962–63. For the first and the last of these the selection was made by Mr. A. E. Popham. The present exhibition is, so to speak, a second edition of the last. But it will, I hope, provide striking evidence of the riches available, that although no single drawing that was exhibited in 1962–63 is included again in 1969, and although there was no conscious intention on the part of the organizers of the first exhibition to follow it with another, the standard is no less high: in some respects, I believe, this second exhibition in America may prove even more popular than the last. In any case, the two catalogues, produced as companion volumes and reproducing well over two hundred drawings, will in conjunction provide a remarkable souvenir of the wealth, quality and variety of this great collection.

The emphasis in the present exhibition is somewhat changed. In 1949 seventy-two mounts in all were shown, of which thirty-two were Italian (including ten of the important collection of birds, animals and plants) and thirty-two Netherlandish. The Italians were nearly all of the fifteenth and sixteenth centuries: Filippino Lippi, Leonardo, Ghirlandaio, Carpaccio, Raphael, Correggio, Parmigianino—nothing later than Barocci and Schedoni. The Netherlandish school was represented chiefly by superb groups of Rubens, Van Dyck and Rembrandt. Among the few German drawings were three magnificent portrait heads, two by Holbein and one by Burgkmair; and under the English school were included specimens of the famous series by Inigo Jones and Wenceslaus Hollar. In the Smithsonian exhibition of 1962, one hundred and fourteen catalogue numbers appeared, many of them repeated from the smaller London show, but with many more of equal importance: among the Italians, there were more of Raphael, more of Parmigianino, and some of Raphael's followers, Giulio Romano, Perino and Peruzzi; Rosso, Bronzino and Primaticcio, Giuseppe Porta, Orsi, Taddeo and Federico Zuccaro increased the small display of the Mannerists, who were now becoming more fashionable; and the Italian seventeenth century, so splendidly represented at Chatsworth, now made its mark with some fine specimens of the Carracci, of Reni, Guercino, Testa and Castiglione.

It is in this last field that the present exhibition is particularly rich; and since that is the direction in which enlightened public taste is turning, I hope that the corollary will be accepted, that there must be fewer of the great rarities of the fifteenth century, especially if repetition is to be avoided. Nevertheless, two pages of Vasari's celebrated *Libro di Disegni* (Nos. 8 and 34), embellished with drawings of an earlier century, are rarities indeed, to say nothing of the early watercolors of birds, animals and plants, of which, as in 1949, a small selection is included (Nos. 1–6). The work of Raphael's followers is represented by more of Giulio Romano and Perino del Vaga; and a group of six drawings by Parmigianino, only one of them shown in 1961 at Manchester and none of them in London in 1949 or in

America in 1962–63, emphasizes the wealth of material by that exquisite draughtsman that is to be found at Chatsworth.

Two other great artists, Rembrandt and Van Dyck, again provide groups of no less than eight and seven respectively, and these I venture to think are as a whole not inferior to the ten of the former and eight of the latter that were sent to the first Chatsworth exhibition in America in 1962. There are no English drawings this time: a special exhibition of the most remarkable of these, the Inigo Jones series, was recently circulated by the International Exhibitions Foundation in the United States, with a catalogue of exceptional interest by Dr. Roy Strong. But there is one feature of the present exhibition that will certainly attract both the student and the amateur—the French drawings, none of which was included in the selection of 1962. Perhaps the recent loss of Claude's *Liber Veritatis*, acquired by the second Duke in 1723, and surrendered to the British Treasury (with Van Dyck's Italian Sketchbook, Holbein's cartoon of Henry VIII, and some important paintings) in part payment of estate duty on the death of the tenth Duke, discouraged the organizers on that occasion. But there are still fine drawings by Claude in the Chatsworth collection, and three of these, one only lately recognized (No. 116), are shown here, with two important examples of Poussin. The *clou* of the French collection, however, is the album of drawings by Callot; and from this several pages have been extracted in order to exhibit drawings that have never been shown separately before (Nos. 111–115).

I have taken the opportunity to select certain drawings that have so far remained anonymous or whose attribution has been disputed in the past. In some cases I have expressed judgments in the catalogue that will, I have no doubt, excite some opposition. I refer particularly to the drawings ascribed to Raphael; for one of these (No. 56) has never before been considered in recent Raphael literature, and the three others have all (to some extent) been questioned by Raphael scholars. Here at least I can boast of some support from distinguished experts, Mr. Popham, Mr. Gere and Dr. John Shearman, whose advice I sought. In other cases, such as No. 7 (Carpaccio?), No. 68 (Titian?), No. 91 (Rembrandt?), and certain of the German drawings, I have ventured to put forward views of my own that have yet to be discussed. Others again are offered to the specialists without definite attributions, as deserving subjects for argument out of which some truth may emerge. That, after all, is one of the results to be hoped for from a public exhibition.

In general, I must acknowledge most gratefully much help from my friends. Mr. Thomas Wragg has been consistently helpful to me in making the selection and collating the recorded comments of those who have had the privilege of working at Chatsworth in the past. Many of these were Mr. Popham's; he indeed has probably studied the collection more thoroughly and with greater experience than any other scholar. In particular, he put at my disposal the catalogue entries for his forthcoming corpus of drawings by Parmigianino. Mr. Gere allowed me to consult the copy of the typewritten Chatsworth catalogue in the British Museum, which is enhanced with notes by Mr. Popham, Mr. Pouncey and himself; and has discussed with me many individual drawings in this exhibition, especially those of the Zuccaro brothers, with whose work he is so familiar. Dr. Shearman, as I have said, has given me valuable advice on the drawings attributed to Raphael. I am grateful to them all for allowing me to quote them in the text.

J. Byam Shaw

COLLECTORS' MARKS

Notes on collectors' marks which occur on more than one mount in the present exhibition.

D WILLIAM CAVENDISH, 2nd Duke of Devonshire (1665–1729) (Lugt No. 718). The 2nd Duke of Devonshire succeeded in 1707 and was the founder of the Devonshire Collection (see introduction to this catalogue).

F NICOLAES ANTHONI FLINCK (1646–1723) (Lugt No. 959). A Director of the India Company of Rotterdam, the son of Govaert Flinck, a pupil of Rembrandt. From his father he inherited a considerable collection of works of art, which he later augmented by purchases. The major portion of his collection of drawings was purchased by the 2nd Duke of Devonshire in 1723. It is possible that other Flinck drawings were acquired by the 3rd Duke of Devonshire at a later date (1754). Two hundred and twenty-five drawings at Chatsworth bear the Flinck mark.

NICOLAS LANIER (1588–1666) (Lugt Nos. 2885 and 2886). Son of Queen Elizabeth's court musician, Lanier filled the same post under Charles I and as a connoisseur of prints and drawings made purchases for the Royal Collections. He also assisted Lord Arundel to form his collection. His two marks were for long confused with those of his patrons.

PHL PROSPER HENRY LANKRINK (1628–1692) (Lugt No. 2090). A German who studied at Antwerp and came to England where he was employed in the studio of Lely. He acted as auctioneer at the first Lely sale in 1688 and bought some of the drawings himself. He also acquired drawings from the collections of Charles I and Lord Arundel. His own collections were sold in London in 1693 and 1694. Forty-four drawings at Chatsworth bear his mark.

PL SIR PETER LELY (1618–1680) (Lugt No. 2092). (Born Pieter van der Faes). Lely came to England in 1641 with William II, Prince of Orange. He reached the height of his fame as a portrait painter under Charles II. He bought largely at the sales following the dispersal of collections after the Civil Wars and also paintings and drawings by Van Dyck from his widow. After Lely's death his collections were sold to pay his debts in 1688 and 1694.

P. Resta Padre SEBASTIANO RESTA (1635–1714) (Lugt No. 2992). A member of the Order of S. Philip Neri at Rome who formed a collection of drawings for Marchetti, Archbishop of Arezzo. This collection of 2638 drawings was acquired by Lord Somers through the Bishop's nephew Talman (the architect of Chatsworth). Resta did not use a mark but annotated the drawings in a characteristic hand.

k.303 *f.2* JOHN, LORD SOMERS (1650–1716) (Lugt No. 2981). Lord Somers, Lord Chancellor of England, acquired the collection formed by Padre Resta in 1710. His prints and drawings were sold at auction in 1717. The drawings from this source at Chatsworth may have been acquired by the 2nd Duke from Crozat, the French dealer, who bought 112 lots at the sale, or perhaps by the 3rd Duke at the sale of Crozat's drawings in 1741. 26 of the drawings at Chatsworth from Lord Somers' collection are inscribed in Padre Resta's hand. Somers did not use a mark but inscribed his drawings with a combination of small letters and numerals.

Catalogue

NOTE ON THE CATALOGUE The entries for the drawings and, in most cases, the illustrations, have been arranged alphabetically under artists within the four schools. Where there is more than one drawing by the same artist, the drawings are arranged in the order of the Chatsworth inventory numbers. Height precedes width in the measurements. The drawings have been reproduced by permission of the Trustees of the Chatsworth Settlement.

EXHIBITIONS

References are given in shortened form to a number of exhibitions, the catalogues of which often provide valuable information. Of these the most significant are the following:

Royal Academy, London, 1927, *Exhibition of Flemish and Belgian Art 1450–1900.*

Royal Academy, London, 1929, *Dutch Art 1450–1900.*

Royal Academy, London, 1930, *Italian Art 1200–1900.*

Royal Academy, London, 1938, *Exhibition of 17th-Century Art in Europe.*

Arts Council, London, 1949, *Old Master Drawings from Chatsworth* (first shown at the Arts Council Gallery in St. James's Square, London, and subsequently in other cities). Catalogue by A. E. Popham.

Royal Academy, London, 1953, *Drawings by Old Masters* (Diploma Galleries). Catalogue by K. T. Parker and J. Byam Shaw.

Royal Academy, London, 1953–54, *Flemish Art 1300–1700.*

Bologna, 1956, *Mostra dei Carracci, Disegni.* Catalogue by Denis Mahon.

Royal Academy, London, 1960, *Italian Art and Britain.*

Newcastle, 1961, King's College Newcastle upon Tyne Department of Fine Art, *The Carracci, Drawings and Paintings.* Catalogue by Ralph Holland.

Manchester, 1961, City Art Gallery, *Drawings from Chatsworth.*

Manchester, 1961, City Art Gallery, *German Art 1400–1800.* Catalogue by F. G. Grossmann.

Bologna, 1968, *Mostra del Guercino, Disegni.* Cat. by Denis Mahon 1969.

America and Canada, 1962–63. *Drawings from Chatsworth* (circulated by the Smithsonian Institution: first shown at the National Gallery Washington, and subsequently in other cities). Catalogue by A. E. Popham.

Catalogue

Italian

Anonymous North Italian

First half of XV century

1 A PEACOCK
Pen and water color, heightened with white.
7 ⅞×7 in.; 20×17.8 cm.
Literature: Waagen, *Treasures of Art in Great Britain*, 1854, iii, p. 360; A. E. Popham, *Catalogue of the Arts Council Exhibition of Chatsworth Drawings*, 1949, pp. 29–30.
Exhibited: Arts Council, London, 1949.

This beautiful drawing, in the manner of Pisanello and surely North Italian of Pisanello's time, is one of a collection of 131 birds, animals and plants (the majority birds) of various dates and schools, originally hung in the "Sketch Gallery" at Chatsworth, then at Compton Place, Eastbourne, and now returned to Chatsworth.

2 A DUCK IN FLIGHT
Pen and water color.
7 ⅞×11 ⅞ in.; 20×30.3 cm.
Literature: as for No. 1.
Exhibited: Arts Council, London, 1949, No. 65.

From the same collection of bird, animal and plant drawings as No. 1, and of the same early group, perhaps by the same hand.

Anonymous Venetian School

Second half of XV century

3 PERIWINKLES AND VIOLETS
Water color and body color; the paper ruled with the stylus.
7×11 ½ in.; 17.8×29.3 cm.
Literature: A. E. Popham, *Catalogue of the Arts Council Exhibition of Chatsworth Drawings*, 1949, p. 29.
Exhibited: Arts Council, London, 1949, No. 66; Royal Academy, London, Drawings by Old Masters, 1953, No. 6.

From the same series as Nos. 1 and 2, but perhaps by a Venetian artist of the school of Giovanni Bellini.

Anonymous Italian

Mid-XVI century

4 A HAWFINCH, WITH ANOTHER STUDY OF THE UNDERSIDE OF THE SAME BIRD
Water color over black chalk. Dated (by the artist?) 1540.
11×8 ⅜ in.; 28×21.5 cm.
Literature: as for No. 1.
Exhibited: Arts Council, London, 1949, No. 68.

From the same collection of bird, animal and plant drawings as No. 1, but perhaps a century later in date than that, and one of many for which the name of Giovanni da Udine (1487–1564) has been plausibly suggested (first by Mrs. Eugenie Strong). Mr. Popham (*loc. cit.*) seems to imply that the date on the *recto* was not written by the artist, but has to do with the MS on the *verso* (which contains a reference to a place near Siena); in which case it would provide only a *terminus post quem*. It seems to me quite likely that it is in fact the actual date of the drawing.

Anonymous Italian

Mid-XVI century

5 A DUCK

Brush and water color, over black chalk.
7 ⅛×11 in.; 18×28 cm.
Literature: as for No. 1.
Exhibited: Arts Council, London, 1949, No. 70.

From the same collection of bird, animal and plant drawings as Nos. 1–4 and belonging to the mid-XVI-century group, in the style of Giovanni da Udine.

Anonymous Italian

XV century

6 A MONKEY SEATED, TO RIGHT

Brush and body color.
15 ¾×11 ½ in.; 40.2×29.3 cm.
Literature: as for No. 1.

The bold technique has the spontaneity of a fresco-painting. This is the largest, and one of the most difficult to attribute, of the whole collection of drawings of birds, animals and plants at Chatsworth. It is different in style to any of the others exhibited here, but is certainly by the hand of an important artist.

Anonymous Venetian School

c. 1520–1525

7 THE EXECUTION OF A SAINT (742)

Pen and brown wash, squared for enlargement.
6×6 ⅞ in.; 15.2×17.4 cm.
Provenance: N. A. Flinck; 2nd Duke of Devonshire.
Literature: Strong, 1902, No. 6; L. Justi, *Giorgione*, 1936, p. 303.
Exhibited: Burlington Fine Arts Club, London, 1912, No. 28A; Brescia, Romanino, 1965, No. 116.

Various names have been suggested for this interesting drawing: Giorgione (Strong, Suida, Justi), Giolfino (Frizzoni) and Romanino (Popham, Gere). The doubts expressed as to the last attribution in the catalogue of the Romanino Exhibition seem to me justified, though it is not clear what the author would suggest as an alternative. The somewhat Germanic style of the soldiers' dress is perhaps suggestive of the Brescian School; but the proportions of the figures are not characteristic of Romanino. Other features of the drawing—the turbaned potentate on the right, the profile of the saint apparently awaiting execution in the center background, and above all the method of drawing with broken contours and cross-hatching with the brush in the background—remind me rather of Carpaccio. It seems to me not impossible that this should be by him at a late stage of his career, after 1520.

Anonymous Florentine School

Late XIV or early XV century

8 A page from Vasari's *Libro di Disegni*: (963)

Recto: PILATE WASHING HIS HANDS
Verso: CHRIST CARRYING THE CROSS
Pen and brown ink.
11 ½×14 ¾ in.; 29.2×37.6 cm.
Both sides enclosed in a decorative border drawn by Vasari. This includes, on the *recto*, a separate smaller drawing of *Four Dogs* (pen and brown ink, 11×17.8 cm.); and on the *verso* the woodcut portrait of Nanni di Banco from Vasari's *Lives of the Painters, Sculptors and Architects* (the brown wash added by hand). The large drawing is inset into Vasari's page, so that both sides are visible.
Provenance: Giorgio Vasari.
Literature: *Old Master Drawings*, XII, 1937, Pl. 9; Degenhart and Schmitt, *Corpus der Italienischen Zeichnungen, 1300–1450*, 1969, I, Nos. 264 and 267 (as by Nanni di Banco or Donatello).

The inscription on the tablet below the *recto* is in Vasari's hand. The drawing is also inscribed: *Donatello*. It is possible that it was intended, as Vasari's attribution suggests, for two sculptured reliefs. The free style is reminiscent of the *sinopie* (preliminary drawings in brush and reddish paint) that have been discovered lately in detaching frescoes from the walls on which they were originally painted.

Mr. David Carritt has made the ingenious suggestion that the drawing of *Four Dogs*, which is clearly of later date than the large drawing, may be by Francesco Pesellino (c. 1422–1457); he compares the dogs in the foreground of the *Triumph of David and Saul*, one of the two fine cassone-panels in the Loyd Collection at Lockinge, Berkshire, England (Cat. 1967, No. 53).

North Italian

late XV century

9 BUST PORTRAIT OF A MAN IN PROFILE TO LEFT (953)
Black chalk, with a little red, washed over, and heightened with white, on buff paper.
13 ⅞×9 ½ in.; 35.3×24.2 cm.
Inscribed right in an early (XVI-century?) hand: *Joha Bellino : Pic : Da Leonardo D. Vinci.*
Literature: Strong, 1902, No. 36.

It is difficult to say how far the interior modelling in this fine portrait is original, but it remains impressive, and is perhaps by a Lombard artist under Venetian influence, as Strong's attribution to Filippo Mazzuola suggests.

Anonymous Emilian (?) School

later XVI century

10 HEAD OF A BEARDED MAN, LOOKING UP TO RIGHT (309)
Black and red chalk.
9 ¼×6 ⅞ in.; 23.5×17.5 cm.
Provenance: N. A. Flinck; 2nd Duke of Devonshire.

The name of Camillo Procaccini (1546–1625) has been suggested for this fine head, and there are large "character" heads in red and black chalk attributed to him in the Accademia, Venice, and also at Windsor Castle and Chatsworth; but they are all noticeably less free in handling.

Niccolò dell'Abbate

c. 1509/1512–1571

11 THE HOLY FAMILY WITH ST. ELIZABETH AND THE INFANT ST. JOHN: THE ANGEL APPEARING TO THE SHEPHERDS IN THE BACKGROUND (190)
Pen and brown wash, heightened with white, over black chalk.
16 1/4 × 13 1/4 in.; 41.5 × 33.4 cm.
Provenance: Sir Peter Lely (Lugt 2092); 2nd Duke of Devonshire (Lugt 718).
Exhibited: Manchester, 1965, No. 248.

Formerly attributed to Primaticcio, but surely by Niccolò dell'Abbate, as Mr. A. E. Popham was the first to suggest.

Francesco Albani

1578–1660

12 AN ALLEGORY: HERCULES AS ATLAS SUPPORTING THE GLOBE, WITH MERCURY AND APOLLO (554)
Pen and brown wash, with body color over black chalk.
11 1/8 × 17 in.; 28.3 × 43.3 cm.
Exhibited: Royal Academy, London, 1938, No. 404.

This fine drawing, very close in style to the late works of Annibale Carracci, was engraved in reverse by Francesco Villamena, probably in Rome in the early years of the XVII century, with the inscriptions *Franciscus Albanus Inventor* and *Franciscus Villamena Fecit*. The figure of Hercules is clearly derived from Annibale's figure in the Camerino Farnese.

I have not been able to identify the arms, which are those of a noble ecclesiastic (but not a cardinal, since the hat, as engraved, has only six tassels). Villamena's engraving shows various differences from the drawing: Hercules's club is added, the villa garden in the background is left out, and Apollo's chariot is drawn by two falcons instead of the horse. The composition was ingeniously adapted, apparently from the print, with appropriate changes of inscription etc., for the *Oxford Almanack* of 1693. These early Almanacks were probably designed by Dean Aldrich of Christ Church, who was almost certainly acquainted with the 2nd Duke of Devonshire.

Baccio Bandinelli

1493–1560

13 STUDY OF A YOUNG MAN IN CONTEMPORARY DRESS (25)
In the background right is a slight sketch of a woman in profile to right.
Pen and brown ink.
15 3/8 × 8 1/2 in.; 39.2 × 21.7 cm.
Inscribed *bacio bandinelli* in a XVI-century hand lower left.
Provenance: N. A. Flinck; 2nd Duke of Devonshire.

The principal study was possibly intended for a David, with a reminiscence of Michelangelo in the pose. It was etched in the reverse direction as the third figure from the left in Jan de Bisschop's *Paradigmata Graphices*, 1671, No. 38. A close copy of the main figure is in the Uffizi (1067 S).

14 THREE SAGES HOLDING TABLETS, AT AN ANTIQUE ALTAR (30)
Pen and brown ink.

15 ¾×11 ⅝ in.; 40×29.5 cm.
Inscribed below: *DI Baccio* (erased) and *DI Michele Agnolo.*
Provenance: N. A. Flinck; 2nd Duke of Devonshire.

The subject is not explained.

Federico Barocci

1526–1612

15 HEAD OF A BOY (355)
Black, red and white chalks.
7 ⅝×8 in.; 20.6×19.4 cm.
Provenance: N. A. Flinck; 2nd Duke of Devonshire.
Literature: F. Schmarsow, *Baroccis Zeichnungen,* 1914, p. 41; H. Olsen, *Federico Barocci,* 1962, p. 174.
Exhibited: Burlington Fine Arts Club, 1925, No. 50 (pl. XLVIII of illustrated catalogue); Manchester, 1961, No. 4.

Connected by Olsen with the *Martyrdom of S. Vitale* in the Brera Gallery, Milan (Olsen, 1962, Pl. 47), which is dated 1583. The boy appears in the center of the composition, looking down into the grave.

16 THE ASSUMPTION OF THE VIRGIN (364)
Pen and brown wash, heightened with white, over black chalk, on grey paper, partly squared for enlargement.
20 ½×14 ⅜ in.; 52.2×36.7 cm.
Provenance: Sir Peter Lely; P. H. Lankrink; 2nd Duke of Devonshire.
Literature: H. Olsen, *Federico Barocci,* 1962, p. 212 and Pl. 110.
Exhibited: Royal Academy, London, Drawings by Old Masters, 1953, No. 106.

A complete and particularly beautiful composition-sketch for the great altarpiece that was still unfinished at Barocci's death, and came through the Albani family to the present owner, Prince Cesare Castelbarco Albani (Olsen, 1962, Pls. 104 and 111). The painting closely follows the Chatsworth drawing. A large number of other studies for the same have been identified by Olsen.

17 THE VISITATION (918)
with another study for the figure of the Virgin on the *verso.*
Black and white chalks on blue paper.
15×10 in.; 38.1×25.3 cm.
Inscribed in a XVII-century hand: *F. Barotsius Urbinas.* Squared.
Provenance: N. A. Flinck; 2nd Duke of Devonshire.
Literature: H. Olsen, *Federico Barocci,* 1962, p. 180 and Pl. 63b.

A study, followed fairly closely in the finished work, for *The Visitation* in the Pozzomiglio Chapel of the Chiesa Nuova, Rome, painted by Barocci 1583–1586 (Olsen, 1962, Pl. 59). Several other drawings for the same are reproduced by Olsen.

Bonifacio De' Pitati

c. 1487–1553

18 Two drawings on one mount: (910)
A THE VIRGIN AND CHILD WITH ST. ROCH AND THE INFANT ST. JOHN THE BAPTIST
Pen and brown ink.
6 ⅜×9 ⅜ in.; 16.3×24 cm.
Provenance: Sir Peter Lely.

B THE SAME SUBJECT WITH TREES IN THE BACKGROUND, AND THE INFANT ST. JOHN ON THE EXTREME RIGHT

Pen and brown ink.

7 5/8×10 1/8 in.; 19.5×25.7 cm.

Provenance: N. A. Flinck; 2nd Duke of Devonshire.

Literature: Vasari Society, 1st Series, v. 10; D. von Hadeln, *Venezianische Zeichnungen der Hochrenaissance*, Pls. 16, 17; H. and E. Tietze, *Drawings of the Venetian Painters*, 1944, p. 116.

These two drawings, apparently acquired from different sources (unless they were originally mounted on the same sheet and all three collectors' marks apply to both), are obviously by the same hand, and very Titianesque in style. The types and the rhythm of the compositions are so close to those of Bonifazio that this attribution, already suggested by Hadeln, may be accepted with some confidence. For A compare the fine (but much damaged) painting at Christ Church, Oxford (Byam Shaw Cat., 1967, No. 85 and Pl. 69).

Luca Cambiaso

1527–1585

19 THE HOLY FAMILY IN THE CARPENTER'S SHOP (384)

Pen and brown ink.

13 5/8×9 1/2 in.; 34.9×24.3 cm.

Provenance: N. A. Flinck; 2nd Duke of Devonshire.

Literature: B. Suida-Manning in *Art Quarterly*, Autumn 1952; the same, *Luca Cambiaso*, 1958, Figs. 220, 221.

Exhibited: Royal Academy, London, Drawings by Old Masters, 1953, No. 129.

Mrs. Suida-Manning (*loc. cit.* 1958) draws attention to a corresponding painting of small dimensions at Wilton House, near Salisbury (Earl of Pembroke, Cat., 1968, No. 202). The composition is one of the most charming creations of this original but not always attractive artist, whose drawings have been so extensively copied and imitated both by contemporary followers and by later forgers.

Domenico Campagnola

c. 1484–1564

20 CHRIST AND ST. PETER WALKING ON THE WATER (253)

Pen and brown ink.

4 5/8×8 1/8 in.; 11.8×20.6 cm.

Provenance: N. A. Flinck.

Literature: H. and E. Tietze, *Drawings of the Venetian Painters*, 1944, p. 125, No. 431.

Described by the Tietzes as "late, shop"; but surely autograph and in fact unusually free and good.

Simone Cantarini

1612–1648

21 DIANA AND ACTAEON (496)

Red chalk.

10 3/4×7 1/2 in.; 27.3×20.9 cm.

Annibale Carracci

1560–1609

22 PAN AND DIANA (414)
Black chalk, pen and wash, heightened with white, on grey ground.
11 1/4×15 5/8 in.; 28.6×40 cm.
Provenance: Padre Sebastiano Resta; Lord Somers; 2nd Duke of Devonshire.
Literature: J. R. Martin, *The Farnese Gallery*, 1965, p. 257, No. 72 (with other literature).

An early idea for the fresco of Pan offering a gift of wool to Diana (Virgil, *Georgics*, III, 391–393), in the vault of the ceiling of the Farnese Gallery in Rome, painted chiefly by Annibale between 1597 and 1603–4. The final fresco is upright in shape; studies nearer to this are in the Louvre and at Windsor Castle (Martin, *op. cit.*, Nos. 73–75).

Richardson's attribution, on the mount below, is to Agostino. It seems to me possible that this is correct, and that the design was improved upon later by his brother.

23 THE MADONNA OF BOLOGNA (427)
Pen and light brown wash.
9 7/8×6 7/8 in.; 25.2×17.5 cm.
Provenance: Sir Peter Lely; N. A. Flinck; 2nd Duke of Devonshire.
Literature: Denis Mahon in *Gazette des Beaux Arts*, 1957, p. 281; J. Byam Shaw, *Paintings by Old Masters at Christ Church Oxford*, 1967, p. 102.
Exhibited: Bologna, 1956, *Disegni*, No. 101; Manchester, 1961, No. 18.

This is one of four known drawings (two at Chatsworth and two in the Albertina, Vienna) for the altarpiece recorded by Bellori (1672, p. 27) as having been painted for the Chapel of the Palazzo Caprara at Bologna, now in the Picture Gallery at Christ Church, Oxford (Byam Shaw, *op. cit.*, No. 183). It is perhaps the best, and, with one of the Albertina drawings, nearest to the finished altarpiece. The second Chatsworth drawing was exhibited in the first exhibition from Chatsworth, circulated in the United States 1962–63 (No. 12).

24 CHRIST CROWNED WITH THORNS (430)
Black chalk and wash, heightened with white over rough black chalk, on blue-grey ground. Indented with the stylus for engraving.
6 3/8×5 1/4 in.; 16.3×13.2 cm.
Provenance: 2nd Duke of Devonshire.

The drawing was considered by H. Bodmer to be a copy from Annibale's etching, Bartsch XVIII, p. 182, No. 3, signed and dated *Annib. Carracius in. et fecit 1606.* It is in fact unquestionably a fine original, as Professor Wittkower observed. The etching is in the reverse direction, and shows some variations: in the print the man on the right (left in the drawing) is putting the reed scepter into Christ's hand, whereas in the drawing he appears to be tying the rope round Christ's wrists.

25 A WOMAN SEATED IN A ROOM (436)
Pen with some light black chalk.
8 5/8×6 5/8 in.; 22×17 cm.
Provenance: Sir Peter Lely; P. H. Lankrink; 2nd Duke of Devonshire.
Literature: J. R. Martin, *The Farnese Gallery*, 1965, p. 252, No. 51 (with other literature).
Exhibited: Newcastle, King's College, 1961, No. 81.

Mr. Rupert Martin (*loc. cit.*) suggests that this may be an early idea for the treatment of the end walls of the Farnese Gallery. Mr. Michael Jaffé believes that it is of later date, 1604–1605, after the painting in the Gallery was finished, when the artist, having been poorly requited by Cardinal Odoardo Farnese, was in a fit of deep depression (*Burlington Magazine*, CIV, 1962, p. 29). It is surely in Annibale's latest style.

26 THE VIRGIN AND CHILD (437)
Pen and brown ink.
7×6 1/8 in.; 17.8×15.6 cm.
Inscribed in a XVII-century hand: *A:Carazzo.*
Provenance: 2nd Duke of Devonshire.
Exhibited: Royal Academy, London, Drawings by Old Masters, 1965, No. 126; Manchester, 1961, No. 17 (as Agostino Carracci).

Professor Rudolf Wittkower attributed the drawing (verbally) to Agostino, but the case is by no means clear. The etching of the *Virgin and Child with the Apple* (Bartsch as Agostino, No. 31) is nearly related, and is inscribed AGO. CA. I., which must mean that the original drawing for that was by Agostino; but the etching is now attributed to Annibale, *c.* 1590 (see Calvesi and Casale, *Incisioni dei Carracci*, 1965, No. 201). For the Chatsworth drawing, I am inclined to favor the old attribution to Annibale at this fairly early date.

27 A CRIPPLE BOY, HALF-LENGTH (443)
Red chalk washed over.
10 3/8×8 7/8 in.; 26.4×22.5 cm.
Inscribed upper left: *disegno di Messer An: Carrazi.* Below this is a hardly legible attribution to *Paulo da Verona* (i.e., Paolo Veronese). On the right: *Non so se Dio m'aiuta.*
Exhibited: Newcastle, King's College, 1961, No. 89.

Surely an early drawing by Annibale, though generally disregarded except by Mr. Ralph Holland in his catalogue of the Newcastle exhibition of 1961. The touching inscription on the right ("I do not know if God helps me") might well be in the artist's hand.

28 LANDSCAPE WITH GYPSIES (462)
Pen and brown ink.
8×11 in.; 20.3×28 cm.

Surely a late drawing by Annibale, though generally ignored in the Carracci literature.

Giovanni Benedetto Castiglione

c. 1600?–1670

29 A BURIAL (622)
Brush and oil color on paper.
16 1/4×11 3/8 in.; 41.4×28.9 cm.
Provenance: P. H. Lankrink; 2nd Duke of Devonshire.

On the date of Castiglione's birth, often given as 1616, see Anthony Blunt, *The Drawings of G. B. Castiglione . . . at Windsor Castle*, 1954, p. 3.

30 ET IN ARCADIA EGO (858)
Pen and brown wash, over black chalk.
8 1/8×11 3/8 in.; 20.7×29 cm.
Provenance: N. A. Flinck; 2nd Duke of Devonshire.

Related in subject to Poussin's celebrated

paintings in the Louvre and at Chatsworth (No. 501). Formerly attributed to Poussin, but certainly by Castiglione.

Giuseppe Cesari, called Cavaliere d'Arpino

1568–1640

31 AN ALLEGORICAL DESIGN, WITH THE ARMS OF THE MEDICI (314)
Red chalk, with some black.
12 1/4×15 5/8 in.; 30×40 cm. (top corners cut)
Provenance: Sir Peter Lely.

Formerly attributed without reason to Palma Giovane, but recognized as the work of the Cavaliere d'Arpino by Mr. Jacob Bean (note in the Chatsworth catalogue). Dr. H. Röttgen confirms this and adds that the drawing was engraved by Philippe Thomassin (Le Blanc, IV, p. 34, no. 70).

Carlo Dolci

1618–1686

32 PORTRAIT OF THE ARTIST'S SHOEMAKER (1053)
Red and black chalks, washed over.
12 3/4×9 1/2 in.; 32.8×24 cm.
Provenance: Padre Resta; Lord Somers (*d. 110*).
Exhibited: Manchester, 1961, No. 26.

The reference *d. 110* at the lower right-hand corner connects with the MS catalogue in the British Museum, generally ascribed to Jonathan Richardson, of the collection of drawings bought by Lord Somers after 1710 from Padre Sebastiano Resta of Milan, sold after Somers' death in 1716. Mr. A. E. Popham has been kind enough to provide the following transcript of Richardson's entry, which itself is transcribed from a note by Padre Resta: "Ecco un altro modo di *Carlin del Dolce* questo Ritratto era del suo Calzolaro. fu discepolo del Vignoli. Carlino era nato nel 1616: mori nel 1686"

Filippino Lippi

1457–1504

33 Two drawings on one mount: (886)

A STUDY OF A YOUNG MAN WEARING A SHORT COAT
Silverpoint, heightened with white body color, on purplish-pink ground.
7 1/8×3 3/8 in.; 18.2×87 cm.
Unidentified collector's mark, Lugt. Suppl. 2908 (Lanière?)

B TWO STUDIES OF A HEAVILY DRAPED FIGURE
Silverpoint, heightened with white body color, on salmon-pink ground.
7 3/4×6 7/8 in.; 19.7×17.4 cm.
Literature: A. Scharf, *Filippino Lippi*, 1935, p. 123, No. 217 (B only).
Exhibited: Royal Academy, London, Drawings by Old Masters, 1953, No. 30 (both).

Neither drawing is catalogued by Berenson. B seems certainly to be by Filippino, still in a somewhat Botticellian style, probably before 1480. It is conceivable that A is also by him at a somewhat later date, though an attribution to Raffaellino del Garbo might also be considered. It is surely by a superior hand to that of the studies mounted by Vasari in No. 34 of the present exhibition. Clearly there was at least one more figure (whose outstretched hand appears at the right margin) to the right of A on the same sheet.

Studio of Filippino Lippi

34 A page from Vasari's *Libro di Disegni*: (961)

A A NUDE MAN SEATED ON THE GROUND
Silverpoint, heightened with white on plum-colored ground.
8 3/4×11 1/8 in.; 19.9×28.5 cm.

B A NUDE MAN IN THE ATTITUDE OF A BEGGAR; and A NUDE MAN IN VIOLENT ACTION
Silverpoint, heightened with white on plum-colored ground.
7 3/4×11 1/4 in.; 19.8×28.3 cm.
The two drawings are laid down on Vasari's page, and surrounded by his decorative border, into which is inserted at the top the woodcut portrait inscribed *Alesso Baldovinetto* from Vasari's *Lives of the Painters*. On the back of the page was originally mounted another drawing, surrounded by a similar border inscribed *Antonello da Messina pitt:*; but this has been torn away, and only a few pen-lines at the left margin and Vasari's border remain.
Literature: Strong, 12 (as by Signorelli); Berenson, 772 G (as by Davide Ghirlandaio, and wrongly described as *recto* and *verso* of the same sheet).

These figure-studies belong to a large and well-known group catalogued by Berenson, on insufficient grounds, as early works of Davide Ghirlandaio. Popham and Pouncey (British Museum Cat., 1950) include several of the same group as of the studio of Filippino Lippi. They are indeed in Filippino's style, but too weak for the master himself.

Giulio Pippi, called Giulio Romano

1499–1546

35 STUDY FOR THE MARRIAGE FEAST OF CUPID AND PSYCHE (96)
Pen and brown ink.
8 1/2×16 1/4 in.; 21.5×41.5 cm.
Provenance: N. A. Flinck; 2nd Duke of Devonshire.
Literature: Hartt, *Giulio Romano*, 1958, No. 174 and Fig. 265.

A preliminary drawing for the long ceiling fresco in the Sala di Psiche of the Palazzo del Te, Mantua. Two figure-groups in the drawing were developed in different parts of the painting—the group with Silenus in the center and the group of nymphs round the table further to the right (Hartt, *op. cit.*, Figs. 254 and 255).

36 DESIGN FOR A FRUIT DISH (100)
Pen and brown wash over black chalk.
13 1/8×12 5/8 in.; 33.6×32.2 cm.
Provenance: 2nd Duke of Devonshire.
Literature: Hartt, *Giulio Romano*, 1958, No. 101 and Fig. 137.

This beautiful drawing is one of the many designs for tableware by the artist, done no doubt for the Ducal court at Mantua. A drawing for a very similar dish, seen in perspective, is also at Chatsworth (Hartt, Fig. 138).

37 THE EROTES OF PHILOSTRATUS (107)
Pen and brown wash, squared.
13 7/8×14 3/4 in.; 35.3×37.8 cm.
Provenance: Sir Peter Lely; 2nd Duke of Devonshire.

Literature: Hartt, *Giulio Romano*, 1958, p. 159, No. 217 and Fig. 354.

Hartt supposes that this may be a sketch for a large painting for the Palazzo del Te, Mantua, which was not executed. It might also have been designed for tapestry. The subject corresponds closely, as Hartt points out, to the description of an ancient painting in Philostratus, *Imagines*, I. 6.

Giovanni Francesco Barbieri, called Guercino

1591–1666

38 THE MADONNA DEL CARMINE OFFERING THE SCAPULA TO S. ALBERTO (519)
Pen and brown wash, with some body color.
16 1/8 × 10 5/8 in.; 41.2 × 26.9 cm.
Literature: D. Mahon, *Il Guercino, Disegni*, 1969 (Cat. of drawings in the Bologna Exh., 1968), pp. 44–46.
Exhibited: Bologna, Guercino Exhibition, 1968, No. 8.

Preliminary study for the early altarpiece now in the Pinacoteca at Cento (Bologna Exh., 1968, No. 7), in which the composition is reversed. Another study, composed in the same direction as the painting, is in the Pierpont Morgan Library, New York (Mahon, *loc. cit.*, No. 9), and a red chalk study for the Virgin and Child only is in the National Gallery of Ireland (*ibid.*, No. 10). A copy of the present drawing is at Christ Church, Oxford. The date, according to Mr. Mahon, is *c.* 1615.

39 LANDSCAPE WITH A FUNERAL PROCESSION (546)
Pen and brown wash.
9 1/8 × 15 3/4 in.; 23.3 × 40.3 cm.
Etched in reverse by Jean Pesne (1623–1700) as No. 5 of a series of fourteen landscapes, all after Guercino, dedicated to the Duke of Modena by the artist's nephews Benedetto and Cesare Gennari.
Literature: D. Mahon, *Il Guercino, Disegni*, 1969 (Cat. of drawings in Bologna Exh., 1968), pp. 9, 183, 188, 189.
Exhibited: Royal Academy, Drawings by Old Masters, 1953, No. 135; Bologna, Guercino Exhibition, 1968, No. 192.

All fourteen of the originals etched by Pesne in Paris are now at Chatsworth; six of them were exhibited at Bologna in 1968. Mr. Denis Mahon supposes that they were sold in England by Benedetto Gennari, who was in London 1674–1688, after the prints had been made. He draws attention to numerous XVIII-century forgeries of this and the others of the series, generally based on a series of prints by L. Mattioli (d. 1747) which are copied (in reverse) from those of Pesne.

Mr. Mahon dates this drawing early, before 1621 when Guercino went to Rome.

40 LANDSCAPE WITH A HORSEMAN AND TWO SOLDIERS BY A RIVER (530)
Pen and brown wash. Etched in reverse by Jean Pesne as No. 9 of the series of fourteen landscapes dedicated to the Duke of Modena.
10 1/2 × 16 5/8 in.; 26.8 × 42.3 cm.
Literature: D. Mahon, *Il Guercino, Disegni*, 1969 (Cat. of drawings in the Bologna Exh., 1968), p. 190.

Exhibited: Manchester, 1961, No. 37; Bologna, Guercino Exhibition, 1968, No. 195.

On the series of drawings, all at Chatsworth, to which this belongs, see the literature cited for No. 39 of this catalogue. Mr. Mahon dates this drawing considerably later than No. 39, and notes that some small additions in black chalk to the tree on the extreme left are probably due to the engraver, or to Benedetto Gennari, since they are included in the print.

Lattanzio da Rimini (attributed to)

Late XV century

41 ST. MARK PREACHING (741)
Pen and brown ink.
Early restorations lower left and right.
Provenance: N. A. Flinck; 2nd Duke of Devonshire.
Literature: D. von Hadeln, *Venezianische Zeichnungen des Quattrocento*, 1925, pp. 64, 65 and Pl. 83.

Strong attributed the drawing to Carpaccio. Von Hadeln (*loc. cit.*) makes a plausible case for supposing that this might be the study for a painting by Lattanzio, dated 1499, which once formed part of a series of four, illustrating the history of St. Mark, in the Church of S. Maria dei Crocicchieri in Venice. Two of these paintings have survived, in Berlin (by Cima) and in the Liechtenstein Collection, and these accord with the present drawing in proportion and scale. But no really comparable works by Lattanzio himself are known.

A very good Rembrantesque drawing in the Pierpont Morgan Library (Benesch, *Rembrandt Drawings*, VI, A.104) is freely copied from this, as Von Hadeln was the first to observe. It will be noted that the Chatsworth drawing belonged to Nicolas Flinck, and probably to his father, Govaert Flinck, who was Rembrandt's pupil.

Carlo Maratti

1625–1713

42 DESIGN FOR A LARGE TITLE-PAGE, WITH AN ALLEGORICAL FIGURE OF THE CATHOLIC CHURCH, AND JUSTICE SEATED BESIDE HER (568)
Pen and wash, over red and black chalk, heightened with white.
19 × 11 1/8 in.; 48.5 × 28.4 cm.
Provenance: 2nd Duke of Devonshire.

The mount is inscribed *Carlo Maratti* in Richardson's hand.

43 PADRE SEBASTIANO RESTA EXAMINING A VOLUME OF DRAWINGS (584)
Red chalk.
10 × 7 3/4 in.; 25.7 × 19.8 cm.
Provenance: Padre Resta; Lord Somers: 2nd Duke of Devonshire.
Literature: A. E. Popham, in *Old Master Drawings*, XI, 1936, p. 5.
Inscribed below the margin line, in Maratti's hand, in ink: *Ritratto dell.Me Reverendo Padre Sebastiano Resta della Congregatione del. Oratorio di San felippo Neri in Roma, che mostra all Sigre Carlo Maratti il presente Libro con le accutissime sue eruditioni—l'ultimo di Marzo= 1689=*; and in black chalk: *furto e Dono dell' Autore.*

The latter inscription seems to imply that the artist extracted the drawing from one of the volumes of Padre Resta's collection, and afterwards gave it back to a subsequent owner of that part of the collection—probably John, Lord Somers, who bought a large quantity of Resta's drawings c. 1710.

Somers died in 1716, three years after Maratti, and his collection was sold at auction in London in the following year. A MS catalogue attributable to one of the Richardsons (probably the elder) is in the British Museum. The small letters and numerals inscribed on the drawings themselves (in this case *K.303*) correspond to that catalogue. Since the Somers sale in 1717, drawings so marked have found their way into collections all over the world; but a very large number is at Chatsworth, and also at Christ Church, Oxford, and it is evident that both the 2nd Duke of Devonshire and General John Guise (who bequeathed his collection to Christ Church in 1765) bought extensively at that sale.

The subject of Maratti's portrait is the celebrated antiquary (1635–1714), who put together and annotated, in many volumes, a very large collection of drawings by old masters, discussed at length by Mr. Popham in an important article in *Old Master Drawings* (*loc. cit.*). One of the volumes has survived intact in the Ambrosiana, Milan.

Another portrait of Resta in profile, in old age, was drawn by P. L. Ghezzi in Rome and etched by Arthur Pond 1738 when in the possession of William Kent.

Pierfrancesco Mola

1612–1666

44 IRIS SENT BY JUNO TO TURNUS (556)
Pen and brown wash, over rough black chalk.
10 1/4 × 16 1/8 in.; 26 × 41.2 cm.
Provenance: 2nd Duke of Devonshire.
Literature: R. Cocke in *Burlington Magazine*, CX, 1968, pp. 558 *ss.* and Fig. 33.

A preliminary sketch for one of the lunette-shaped compartments of the ceiling of the Sala dell' Aria in the Palazzo Pamphili at Valmontone, near Rome, painted by Mola in the 1650's. These paintings were destroyed to make room for the work of Mattia Preti, in 1661; but Dr. Cocke (*loc. cit.*) has been able to reconstruct their scheme and general appearance from contemporary records and existing drawings. The present subject, which derives from *Aeneid* IX, 2–4, was substituted by Mola for *The Forge of Vulcan*, a preliminary drawing for which is also at Chatsworth (Cocke, *loc. cit.*, Fig. 32).

Jacopo Palma, called Palma Giovane

1544–1628

45 THE TRANSLATION OF THE BODY OF ST. LUCY TO VENICE BY THE DOGE ENRICO DANDOLO (315)
Pen and brown wash.
11 × 15 1/2 in.; 28.2 × 39.8 cm.
Inscribed *In Sta Lucia in Venetia* and *Palma* in an early hand.
Literature: Ridolfi, *Maraviglie*, 1648 (ed. Hadeln, 1924), II, 185; H. and E. Tietze, *Drawings of the Venetian Painters*, 1944, p. 201, No. 865.

An important record of one of the paintings executed by Palma Giovane for the chapel of St. Lucy, erected by the Florentine Donato Baglioni in 1592 in the church of S. Lucia in Venice. The church was destroyed in 1863 to make room for the railway station. "Il Palma vi dipinse la palla, come anche le due tele laterali, ove in una espresse la Santa in estasi all a tomba di Sant' Agata, e nell'altra la traslazione dell detto Corpo in Venezia" (*Cronica Veneta*, 1736, p. 328).

46 THREE HEADS, INSCRIBED AS PORTRAITS OF THE PAINTERS JACOPO BASSANO, PAOLO VERONESE AND PIETRO MALOMBRA (1064)
Pen and brown ink.
5 3/4×3 5/8 in.; 14.5×9.4 cm.
(There are figure-studies in the same medium on the *verso*.)
Provenance: Padre Sebastiano Resta; Lord Somers; 2nd Duke of Devonshire.

Mr. Frits Lugt owns a small volume of drawings by Palma Giovane, in contemporary binding, that contains fifty portrait-heads of artists, arranged three on a page in the same way as on the present sheet, and with similar figure-studies on the back. One of the pages (exhibited, *Le Dessin Italien dans les Collections Néerlandais*, 1962, No. 126 and Pl. XCI) has three portraits that might all be of the same persons as here; but the head at the top of the page, which is certainly the same as that inscribed *Jacopo Bassano* in the Chatsworth drawing, is there inscribed IACº TE'Tº (Tintoretto), and that identification seems preferable (cf. Tintoretto's late self-portrait in the Louvre). If the heads called Paolo Veronese in both the Lugt and the Chatsworth drawings are rightly identified, the one here must represent him at a more advanced age, but both heads in these drawings show decidedly more hair on the forehead than other supposed self-portraits of Veronese (See L. Goldscheider, *Five Hundred Self-Portraits*, 1937, Pls. 135–138). It seems likely that the inscriptions, though of fairly early date in both cases, are not always reliable. Some of the portraits in the Lugt volume must be derivative, since they include such artists as Raphael, Giulio Romano and Perino del Vaga; but the Venetian artists named here were all living in Palma's working lifetime. Malombra, the youngest by far, was born in 1556; Veronese died in 1588, Bassano in 1592, and Tintoretto in 1594.

Francesco Mazzuola, called Il Parmigianino

1503–1540

47 A SHEPHERD ASLEEP, UNDER A TREE (240B)
Pen and brown ink.
6 3/4×6 1/4 in.; 17.1×15.9 cm. (cut diagonally on right)
Exhibited: Manchester, 1961, No. 41.

Once attributed to Titian, but certainly by Parmigianino, as Mr. A. E. Popham was the first to observe.

48 HEAD OF A BOY IN PROFILE TO RIGHT (778)
Pen and brown ink.
4 1/2×3 5/8 in.; 11.6×9.4 cm.
Inscribed in an early hand *Parmesano*.
Provenance: Earl of Arundel (?) (etched by Vorsterman or Van der Borcht); 2nd Duke of Devonshire.
Literature: Vasari Society, 1st Series, VII, 11.

The drawing is clearly a portrait, and of late date. Mr. Popham observes that the boy bears some resemblance to one of the sons of the

Contessa di San Secondo in the family group in the Prado Gallery, Madrid, painted by Parmigianino 1533–1535 (Freedberg, *Parmigianino*, 1950, Fig. 143).

49 THE VIRGIN AND CHILD, HALF-LENGTH (781)

Red chalk over preliminary indications with the stylus.

4 3/8×3 1/2 in.; 11.2×8.8 cm.

Provenance: Sir Peter Lely; N. A. Flinck; 2nd Duke of Devonshire.

Literature: Vasari Society, 1st Series, VI, 10.

Exhibited: Royal Academy, London, Drawings by Old Masters, 1953, No. 73; Royal Academy, 1960, No. 587.

There are indications of the head and shoulders of St. Joseph at upper right, and the subject must have been originally conceived as a *Holy Family*; but the artist's insistence on the compact oval composition of the two principal figures, and their almost Raphaelesque interrelation, suggests that the idea of a third figure was soon abandoned.

A very early drawing, much influenced by Correggio; according to Mr. Popham, probably before 1523, when the Parmigianino left Parma for Rome.

50 A GROUP OF PUTTI, WITH TREES BELOW on the *verso*, MUSICIAN ANGELS IN THE CLOUDS (792)

Pen and light brown wash.

4 7/8×7 1/8 in.; 12.4×18.2 cm.

Provenance: 2nd Duke of Devonshire.

Exhibited: Royal Academy, London, Drawings by Old Masters, 1953, No. 69.

Professor J. Wilde has observed that this is part of the same sheet as a drawing in the Fogg Art Museum (Sachs-Mongan Cat., 1940, No. 136 and Fig. 81), which continues (below) the composition on the *recto*. The rough sketch on the *verso*, according to Mr. Popham, seems to be developed in a drawing of the *Adoration of the Shepherds* in the Metropolitan Museum, which must date from the artist's Roman period (1524–1527).

51 BUST OF A BEARDED MAN IN PROFILE TO LEFT (794)

Pen and brown ink.

6 1/2×4 5/8 in.; 16.5×11.8 cm.

Provenance: Earl of Arundel (?); 2nd Duke of Devonshire.

The head was etched in reverse by Lucas Vorsterman, which suggests that it was then in the Arundel Collection. Mr. Popham points out that an almost identical head (perhaps a "type" rather than a portrait) appears at the lower right corner of a sheet at Parma with a study of a dead mouse (Copertini, *Il Parmigianino*, II, Pl. ciii).

52 A SATYRESS ASLEEP, UNDER A TREE (1088)

Black chalk, with white (oxidized) on bluish paper.

7 7/8×6 1/4 in.; 20×15.8 cm.

Inscribed *Andrea Schiavon* in an early hand, lower left.

Provenance: Sir Peter Lely; 2nd Duke of Devonshire.

A very early drawing, probably before 1523, first attributed to Parmigianino by Mr. John Gere. The attribution is accepted by Mr. Popham.

Pietro Buonaccorsi, called Perino Del Vaga

1501–1547

53 STUDY FOR AN ALTAR-PIECE—THE VIRGIN AND CHILD ENTHRONED, WITH SS. GREGORY (?) AND JAMES (?), AND A FAMILY OF DONORS (152)

Pen and brown wash, heightened with body color, over black chalk. Squared for enlargement and partly pricked for transfer. The lower left corner made up by a later hand.

14×10 in.; 35.8×25.4 cm. (arched above).

Provenance: Sir Peter Lely; 2nd Duke of Devonshire.

A fine example of Perino's mature style.

54 THE HOLY FAMILY WITH ST. PETER INTRODUCING A DONOR (159)

Pen and brown wash, heightened with body color.

8 7/8×6 3/8 in.; 22.5×16.3 cm.

A characteristic drawing of Perino's maturity, perhaps done in Genoa between 1528 and 1536.

Raphael

1483–1520

55 MERCURY AND PSYCHE (55)

Red chalk, over indications with the stylus.

10 1/2×8 7/8 in.; 26.9×22.7 cm.

Provenance: 2nd Duke of Devonshire.

Literature: Fischel, *Raphael*, 1948, p. 185 and Pl. 212 (as by a pupil of Raphael).

Study for the two figures on the extreme left of the ceiling-fresco in the Farnesina, finished by Raphael and his assistants for Agostino Chigi in 1518.

Drawings of this type have been frequently ascribed to Giulio Romano, who must certainly have participated in the work at the Farnesina. Fischel (*loc. cit.*) is severe on the draughtsman of the present sheet, who, he says, set an antique head of Hermes on "a *torso* of a youth from the Casa Galli" which appears at the right of one of the drawings in Marten van Heemskerck's Roman Sketch-book in Berlin (Fischel, *op. cit.*, Fig. 213A); and he adds that Raphael improved the head in the fresco. I cannot follow this; the head in the drawing seems to me to be particularly good, and to compare favorably with that in the painting. It is well known, in any case, that the Farnesina paintings were extensively restored under the direction of Carlo Maratti at the end of the XVII century. Dr. John Shearman, who once tentatively ascribed the Chatsworth drawing to Penni (Vienna *Jahrbuch*, LX, 1964, p. 96), is now inclined to accept it as Raphael's own.

56 STUDY OF ONE OF THE MARBLE HORSES OF THE QUIRINAL (657)

Red chalk, over indications with the stylus, with notes of measurement by the artist in pen and ink.

8 5/8×10 3/4 in.; 21.8×27.2 cm.

Provenance: Sir Peter Lely; 2nd Duke of Devonshire.

Mr. John Gere and Dr. John Shearman both share my opinion that this beautiful drawing, which has not, so far as I can discover, been noticed in the Raphael literature, may well be by Raphael himself. It represents the so-called "Opus Praxitelis," which is less extensively restored than the other horse.

57 STUDIES FOR THE MADONNA OF THE MEADOW (723)
on the *verso*, A MADONNA AND CHILD after Michelangelo.
Pen and brown ink.
9¾×7⅝ in.; 25×19.4 cm.
Provenance: Sir Peter Lely; 2nd Duke of Devonshire.
Literature: Vasari Society, 1st Series, VI, 7; O. Fischel, *Raphaels Zeichnungen*, III, No. 117 (with earlier literature); A. E. Popham, *Italian Drawings at the Royal Academy*, 1930 (1931), No. 124.
Exhibited: Royal Academy, London, 1930, No. 467; No. 576 at the same, 1960.

A first idea for the *Madonna im Grünen* in Vienna, of 1505. Studies on the *recto* of a sheet in the Albertina (Cat. III, 50) show the composition developed a little further. Fischel considered that the Chatsworth drawing had been worked up, possibly by another hand; but his doubts seem hardly justified. The figure of the little St. John at top left occurs again on the *verso* of the Albertina sheet.

According to Fischel, the drawing on the Chatsworth *verso*, a slight sketch of Michelangelo's *tondo* now in the Royal Academy, London, is no more than a copy of a drawing in the Louvre (Fischel 108), which is itself, again according to him, only an "old facsimile" of Raphael. This is not borne out by comparison of the two drawings: the Chatsworth *verso* is somewhat nearer to Michelangelo's original. It has undeniable weaknesses, but considering the practical difficulty of sketching from a sculptured relief, I am not convinced that it is not from Raphael's hand. Dr. John Shearman shares my view.

58 STUDY FOR THE TRANSFIGURATION, WITH NUDE FIGURES (904)
Red chalk, over preliminary indications with the stylus, squared for enlargement.
9⅝×13¾ in.; 24.6×35 cm.
Provenance: 2nd Duke of Devonshire.
Literature: Strong, 1902, No. 25.
Exhibited: Royal Academy, London, Drawings by Old Masters, 1953, No. 44; Manchester, 1961, No. 54.

Some doubt has been expressed in the past as to the authenticity of this fine drawing; but in consideration of the fact that the figures are studied in the nude, and that there are notable *pentimenti* (especially in the figure of Elijah on the right), the simple explanation would seem to be that it is a working study for Raphael's late altarpiece now in the Vatican Gallery, and some may take a more positive view of the authorship of the drawing, even if occasional faults are undeniable. The alternative theory would be that in the preparation of Raphael's later altarpieces some of the preliminary drawings were actually carried out by his most gifted pupils, such as G. F. Penni and Giulio Romano, under the master's direction and for his use.

School of Raphael

(G. F. Penni ?)

59 CONSTANTINE, ADDRESSING HIS TROOPS, STARTLED BY THE VISION OF THE CROSS IN THE SKY (175)

Pen and brown wash over black chalk, with body color, partly squared for enlargement.
9 1/8×16 1/4 in.; 23.2×41.5 cm.
Provenance: Sir Peter Lely; N. A. Flinck; 2nd Duke of Devonshire.
Exhibited: Royal Academy, London, 1960, No. 570.

This famous "Raphael," which fetched the vast price of £100 at the Lely Sale in 1688, is at present attributed to Perino del Vaga at Chatsworth, but is almost certainly by Penni, who, with Giulio Romano, was an executor of the master's estate at his death. It is a study for the fresco of this subject in the Sala di Constantino in the Vatican. The fresco is often attributed to Giulio Romano (Hartt, *Giulio Romano*, 1958, II, Pl. 57), but the Chatsworth drawing is certainly not by Giulio. It is evidently cut at the top, so that the angels with the cross do not appear.

The account of the sale in 1688 in the autobiography of Roger North, who was Lely's executor, includes the following references to this drawing and (probably) to the 2nd Duke of Devonshire: "I remember a lord, now a duke, said, 'Damn me, what care I whether the owner bids or not as long as I can tell whether I wish to buy, and for what'.... There was half a sheet that Raphael had drawn upon with umber and white, that we called washed and heightened: a tumult of Roman soldiery, and Caesar upon a *suggestum* with officers appeasing them. This was rallied at first, and some said 6d, knowing what it would come to; but then £10, £30, £50, and my quarrelsome lord bid £70, and Sonnius £100 for it, and had it. The lord held up his eyes and hands to heaven, and prayed to God he might never eat bread cheaper" (*The Lives of the Norths*, ed. Jessop, 1890, pp. 199–200). Sonnius was one of the auctioneer's agents. Whether or not the "quarrelsome lord" was the future Duke of Devonshire, the Duke acquired the drawing in the end, with the Flinck Collection, in 1723.

Girolamo Romanino

1484/7–1562 (or after)

60 STUDY OF AN EXECUTIONER (759)
Pen and brown wash heightened with body color, over red chalk on blue paper.
10 1/2×7 1/2 in.; 26.7×19.2 cm.
Provenance: N. A. Flinck; 2nd Duke of Devonshire.
Literature: Strong, *Chatsworth Drawings*, 1902, No. 67 (as by Callisto da Lodi); Catalogue of Romanino Exhibition, Brescia, 1965, p. 232.

The attribution of this fine drawing to Romanino, which seems perfectly convincing, is said in the catalogue of the Romanino Exhibition (1965) to be due to F. Kossoff. It was suggested independently by A. E. Popham.

Romanino (?)

61 A FAMILY SEATED ROUND A TABLE (1054)
Pen and brown wash. (Right edge repaired.)
7×8 in.; 18.1×20.3 cm.
Provenance: 2nd Duke of Devonshire.

First attributed to Romanino by A. E. Popham.

Bartolomeo Schedoni

c. 1570–1615

62 A MOTHER AND CHILD
(552)
Black chalk, washed over, slightly heightened with white, on blue-grey paper.
16 1/8 × 12 1/2 in.; 41 × 31.8 cm.
Provenance: Lanière; N. A. Flinck; 2nd Duke of Devonshire.
Literature: *Old Master Drawings*, I (1926), Pl. 19.

Formerly attributed to Guercino, but rightly identified by Campbell Dodgson (*loc. cit.*). Another excellent figure-study by Schedoni is at Chatsworth, No. 367 (exhibited, *Drawings from Chatsworth*, U.S.A., 1962–63, No. 67).

Francesco Solimena

1657–1747

63 HELIODORUS DRIVEN FROM THE TEMPLE (626)
Pen and grey wash over black chalk.
14 7/8 × 21 3/8 in.; 38 × 54.7 cm.

This important drawing is Solimena's study for the great fresco, signed and dated 1725, in the church of the Gesù Nuovo at Naples (F. Bologna, *Solimena*, 1959, p. 259 and Fig. 167). A painted *bozzetto* is in the Louvre (*ibid.*, p. 272 and Fig. 166); and small versions with considerable variations are in the Galleria Nazionale in Rome (*ibid*, p. 273 and Fig. 165) and in the Turin Gallery (*ibid.*, p. 276). The Chatsworth drawing probably precedes the Louvre oil-sketch, and differs from this and from the fresco in various details, particularly in the figures in the background. Instead of the naked beggar in the lower left corner, both the fresco and the oil-sketch show a boy, with the dog to his left.

64 THE VIRGIN AND CHILD IN THE CLOUDS, CROWNED BY AN ANGEL, WITH SS. MONICA, AUGUSTINE AND DOMINIC, AND THE SOULS IN PURGATORY BELOW
(627)
Pen and grey wash, over black chalk.
14 1/4 × 9 3/4 in.; 36.3 × 24.7 cm.
Provenance: 2nd Duke of Devonshire.

A study for an altarpiece. No painting of this composition seems to exist, but the subject of St. Monica receiving the girdle, and St. Augustine kneeling on the left, occurs in the altarpiece in the church of S. Maria Egiziaca a Forcella in Naples, dating probably 1696. See Bologna, *Solimena*, 1959, Fig. 106 and p. 263.

Parri Spinelli

c. 1387–1453

65 *Recto*: CHRIST AND THE WOMAN TAKEN IN ADULTERY
Verso: PILGRIMS AT A SHRINE
(703)
Pen and brown ink, over black chalk.
11 1/4 × 8 1/8 in.; 28.8 × 20.8 cm.
Literature: Vasari Society, 2nd Series, VI, 2, 3; Berenson, 1837 D; Degenhart and Schmitt, 1969, I, No. 212.
Exhibited: Royal Academy, London, 1953, No. 1.

Professor Degenhart and Dr. Annegrit Schmitt (*loc. cit.*) were the first to point out that the *recto* of this sheet originally formed the right half of a composition which is completed on the *recto* of a sheet now in the Uffizi (*ibid.*, No. 211). A similar double sheet by Parri still intact, with a continuous composition on the *recto* and two independent studies on the *verso*, is also in the Uffizi (*ibid.*, No. 213).

Pietro Testa

1617–1650

66 AN ALLEGORY OF THE CROSS (602A)

Pen and brown ink over light black chalk.

17 3/8×11 in.; 34.4×27.8 cm. (lower left corner cut)

Inscribed by the artist below: *contorni assai assai assai schietti e fondi* (?) *poche ombre. pietro testa.*

Provenance: P. H. Lankrink; also unidentified collector's mark, Lugt 2908 (Lanière?).

The inscription is obscure. The signature is in a darker ink but may be in the same hand. The drawing is probably the first of three preliminary studies, all at Chatsworth, for Testa's etching, Bartsch XX, p. 216, No. 4, which was dedicated to Cassiano dal Pozzo. Of the others, one (602C) is inscribed below *Incidatur* with a signature which I cannot read (evidently that of someone to whom the design was submitted for approval); and the third (602B) ,which is the most careful and was most closely followed (so far as it goes) in the etching, has the figures of the Virgin and the Child pasted onto it from a separate sheet. All three are in reverse to the print and illustrate the great care taken by the artist in preparing a design for etching.

Domenico Tintoretto

c. 1560–1635

67 THE VIRGIN AND CHILD IN THE CLOUDS PRESENTING A ROSARY TO A SAINT; A BISHOP AND OTHER FIGURES BELOW (273)

Brush and oil monochrome on blue paper.

16×9 3/4 in.; 40.7×24.9 cm.

The old mount is inscribed *Tintoretto*, in Richardson's hand.

Provenance: Padre Sebastiano Resta; Lord Somers; 2nd Duke of Devonshire.

Literature: H. and E. Tietze, *Drawings of the Venetian Painters*, 1944, p. 260, No. 1483.

In the same bold free style as the large collection of drawings from a XVII-century album in the British Museum, for the most part formerly attributed to Jacopo Tintoretto, but later (by Hadeln, *Venezianische Handzeichnungen der Spätrenaissance*, 1926) to his son Domenico. They show him to have been a considerable artist in his own right.

Attributed to Titian

c. 1477–1576

68 PASTORAL LANDSCAPE WITH A NUDE WOMAN ON THE RIGHT, HER HEAD ENVELOPED IN A CLOAK (750)

Pen and brown ink, touched with body color.

7 5/8×11 3/4 in.; 19.5×29.8 cm.

Inscribed *Titiano* in a XVII-century hand.

Literature: Strong, *Chatsworth Drawings*, 1902, No. 59.

Exhibited: Royal Academy, London, Drawings by Old Masters, No. 89.

I believe that this fine landscape, which has been generally neglected in the literature on Venetian drawings and is not included in the Tietzes' work, is by Titian himself, in his early, Giorgionesque phase. It is much more dramatic in the lighting of the sky and distance, and much less mannered in execution, than anything of Domenico Compagnola, to whom it was formerly attributed at Chatsworth; and the mysterious woman with the cloak is decidedly reminiscent of the famous *Concert champêtre* in the Louvre, alternatively attributed to Giorgione and to the young Titian.

Compare the large and beautiful woodcut after Titian, *Landscape with a Milkmaid* (Mauroner, *Le Incisioni di Tiziano*, 1943, Pl. 29; Passavant, VI, 242, 96); and the related drawing at Bayonne (Mauroner, *ibid.*, Pl. 30), surely by the same hand as the Chatsworth sheet.

Francesco Vanni

1553–1610

69 THE MADONNA IMMACOLATA, WITH FIVE SAINTS (370)
Black and red chalk, washed over.
15×9 7/8 in.; 38.5×25 cm.
Provenance: Lanière; N. A. Flinck; 2nd Duke of Devonshire.

The three saints right and center are St. Jerome, St. Francis and St. John the Baptist. The soldier saint in the background might be St. Ansanus, and the one kneeling on the left Bernardo Tolomei, who appears with the book and three *monti* in Vanni's *Canonization of St. Catherine of Siena.*

The attribution has been doubted, but the drawing seems characteristic of Vanni and is particularly beautiful in composition.

70 A WOMAN, HALF-LENGTH, AND OTHER STUDIES (659)
Black and some red chalk.
9 5/8×7 5/8 in.; 24.5×19.3 cm.
Provenance: N. A. Flinck; 2nd Duke of Devonshire.

An attribution to Casolani has been suggested, but the drawing seems too good for that indifferent artist, and less mannered in style than his most characteristic works.

Vanni (?)

71 THE HOLY FAMILY (1087)
Red and black chalk.
10 1/4×7 1/4 in.; 26×18.5 cm.
Provenance: N. A. Flinck.

This attractive drawing has been attributed to Barocci, but is not quite in his style. There is an XVIII-century attribution to Vanni on the back of the mount, and it may be by him in his early, most Baroccesque phase.

Giorgio Vasari

1511–1574

72 DESIGN FOR A CEILING (180)
Pen and light brown wash.
12 1/8×18 1/2 in.; 30.8×47.3 cm.
Provenance: 2nd Duke of Devonshire.
Literature: *Revue de l'Art*, 1968, p. 90, No. 7.

This important drawing is clearly inspired, in its general plan and to some extent in its iconography, by Michelangelo's ceiling of the Sistine Chapel. It has lately been identified by Catherine Monbeig-Goguel and Walter Vitzthum (*loc. cit.*) as a design for the ceiling of the refectory of the Jesuit College at Cortona, executed mainly by Cristoforo Gherardi, from drawings by Vasari, in 1554. Though the connection is perhaps not very obvious it is noticeable that the sacrifices of the Prophets named in the Chatsworth drawing are the subjects of the paintings on the wall-spaces between the vaulting (Barocchi, *Vasari*, 1964, pls. 49, 50).

Paolo Caliari, called Veronese

1528–1588

73 A POLITICAL ALLEGORY (278)

Pen and brown wash, heightened with white over black chalk, on green ground.

17 5/8 × 22 7/8 in.; 43.7 × 58.3 cm.

Literature: H. and E. Tietze, *Drawings of the Venetian Painters*, 1944, p. 355, No. 2165.

This very important drawing is inadequately described by the Tietzes as School of Veronese ("a typical shop production"), without explanation of the subject, which has been supposed (certainly wrongly) to be *The Dispute of St. Catherine*, but most probably refers to some important historical occasion, perhaps the Peace of Cateau Cambrésis in 1559.

Emperor, Pope and Doge, seated on the left with their Courtiers, Cardinals and Senators respectively behind them, and their symbolic animals, eagle, wolf and lion, below, are receiving an allegorical figure of Peace(?), while three Saints (including St. Mark) in the clouds above throw down olive branches into the hall below. Drummers and soldiers, and further allegorical figures, including Neptune, are on the right.

The elaborate architecture, rather schematically drawn with the help of the ruler, may well be the work of a studio assistant, but the principal figures and the finishing touches are surely by Veronese himself. There is some damage through the center, and some of the contours have been redrawn (*e.g.*, the three putti holding arms, right center).

Federico Zuccaro

1540–1609

74 THE CORONATION OF THE VIRGIN, WITH SS. LAWRENCE, DAMASUS, PETER AND PAUL IN THE FOREGROUND, AND THE MARTYRDOM OF ST. LAWRENCE IN THE BACKGROUND (199)

Pen and brown wash over black chalk, heightened with white (main composition only). The border is on separate pieces of paper attached to the main composition.

22 1/2 × 16 3/4 in.; 57.3 × 42.7 cm.

Inscribed *Frederico Zucchero* below in a XVII-century hand. There is a date 1570 in lower right-hand corner.

Provenance: Lanière; N. A. Flinck.

Literature: J. Gere in *Burlington Magazine*, CVIII, 1966, pp. 341 *ss*.

This highly elaborate drawing is a record of the altarpiece originally planned by Taddeo Zuccaro for the Church of S. Lorenzo in Damaso, Rome, and finished by his younger brother Federico after Taddeo's death. It was almost certainly drawn for Cornelis Cort, the engraver, whose print corresponds closely in the reverse direction, framework and all. Mr. Gere observes that Federico's personal device, a sugar-loaf (*zuccaro*) with lilies growing out of it, here introduced at the lower corners of the frame, would have been considered quite unsuitable to the altarpiece in the church.

In the article cited above, Mr. Gere publishes several drawings by Taddeo Zuccaro which he connects with this project, and refers to three other drawings by Federico, in the Louvre, at Bremen and in the possession of Mrs. D. Appleton in London. The Bremen drawing (560 × 425 mm.) has the framework, as in the present example and in Cort's engraving (J. Bierens de Haan, *L'Oeuvre gravé de Cornelis Cort*, 1948, No. 141, Pls. 41, 42).

75 PORTRAIT OF AN OLD LADY, HALF-LENGTH (734)
Black and red chalks.
9 3/4 × 5 1/2 in.; 25.2 × 14.1 cm.
Provenance: 2nd Duke of Devonshire.
Literature: Vasari Society, 1st Series, VI, 13.
Exhibited: Royal Academy, London, Drawings by Old Masters, 1953, No. 125.

The study was used for a figure in the group of portraits of Zuccaro's family, colleagues and friends introduced into one of the compartments of the cupola of the Duomo at Florence (west side; see the reproduction in D. Heikamp's important article in *Paragone*, No. 205, 1967, Pl. 15).

76 PORTRAIT OF A BEARDED MAN, HALF-LENGTH (735)
Black and red chalks.
10 × 5 3/4 in.; 25.5 × 14.6 cm.
Provenance: 2nd Duke of Devonshire.
Literature: Vasari Society, 1st Series, VI, 12.

This excellent drawing, though exactly in the style of the preceding drawing, does not seem to have been used in the group of portraits in the cupola of the Duomo at Florence, where the old lady appears. It may, however, represent one of Federico's family or friends, and may have been done with that group in mind.

Taddeo Zuccaro

1529–1566

77 A GROUP OF HORSES AND MEN, FACING RIGHT (193)
Pen and brown wash, with body color.
19 1/2 × 15 1/4 in.; 49.7 × 38.9 cm.
Provenance: Lanière (?); Nicola Haym (*c.* 1679–1729).
Literature: The drawing will be catalogued as No. 18 in Mr. John Gere's book on Taddeo Zuccaro as a draughtsman, to be published in 1969.
Exhibited: Royal Academy, London, Drawings by Old Masters, 1953, No. 124.

A study for the left-hand side of an *Adoration of the Magi*, datable, according to Mr. Gere, in the early 1550's. He suggests that this may be an early project for the decoration of the Mattei Chapel of S. Maria della Consolazione in Rome, which Taddeo executed between 1553 and 1556. Mr. Craig Smyth identified as by Taddeo a rougher study for the same composition, formerly attributed to Titian in the Uffizi (inv. 1731 F, reproduced in the catalogue of the Uffizi exhibition of Zuccaro drawings, 1966, No. 11).

Dutch and Flemish

Paul Brill

1554–1626

78 ROMAN LANDSCAPE WITH RUINED MEDIAEVAL BUILDINGS OVERGROWN BY TREES (698)
Pen and brown and grey wash.
10 7/8×16 5/8 in.; 27.5×42.4 cm.
Dated lower left 1615, and inscribed *P. Bril* below center.
Provenance: 2nd Duke of Devonshire.
Exhibited: Royal Academy, London, 1929, No. 542.

An important late example of Brill, formerly attributed to Claude, with whose landscape drawings it makes an interesting comparison.

Sir Anthony van Dyck

1599–1641

79 A STUDY OF COWS (964)
Pen and brown ink, with a little brown wash.
12 1/2×20 1/4 in.; 31.8×51.5 cm.
Inscribed below in a XVII-century hand, *Ant. van Dyck* (partly cut off).
Provenance: N. A. Flinck.
Literature: Max Rooses, *L'Oeuvre de Rubens*, No. 1584 (as Rubens).
Exhibited: Royal Academy, London, 1938, No. 609 (as Rubens).

Of three known versions of this drawing, the present example is surely the best, as Rooses and Colvin both maintained, and as Mr. A. E. Popham also believes. The other two are both in the British Museum; one of these (Hind, *Catalogue of Dutch and Flemish Drawings*, II, p. 45, No. 122) has generally been admitted to be an inferior copy; but the other (Hind, No. 118, Vasari Society, 2nd Series, VIII, 12; Glück and Haberditzl, *Rubens Handzeichnungen*, No. 136) has been supposed to be an original study by Rubens for the *Landscape with Cows* at Munich, a late work of *c.* 1636–1638. It is noticeably inferior to the present drawing in the rendering of the bushes left and center, and the more slightly indicated animals upper left and right.

I believe, however, that the Chatsworth drawing is not by Rubens but by Van Dyck, as the old inscription says. This leaves its relationship to Rubens' painting more difficult to explain, unless we are to suppose that Rubens used on this occasion a drawing by his most gifted pupil, which he had by him in the studio. In fact only the cow on the left, with head turned away, and the lightly sketched one, seen from the back, at upper right, correspond to any of those in the painting at Munich.

The composition was engraved by Paul Pontius in Rubens' Drawing-Book (Rooses 1229, No. 16).

80 CHRIST CARRYING THE CROSS:
verso A SKETCH OF THE BRAZEN SERPENT (988)
Pen and brown and grey wash, over black chalk with some red chalk; the *verso* in pen only.
7 3/4×6 1/8 in.; 19.7×15.6 cm.
Inscribed on the *verso* in a XVII- or XVIII-century hand: *P.N. No. 18. Vandyke.*
Provenance: N. A. Flinck.
Literature: Van Gelder, Brussels Museums Bulletin, 1961, pp. 3–18; Vey, *Van Dyck Zeichnungen*, 1962, No. 10 and Figs. 14, 15.

Exhibited: Antwerp and Rotterdam, 1960, No. 9.

A study for one of Van Dyck's earliest works, the *Christ Carrying the Cross* in the Church of St. Paul at Antwerp (1617–1618), one of a series of fifteen paintings executed by various artists (among them Rubens, Jordaens, Hendrick van Balen and Cornelis de Vos) for the north side-aisle of the church where they still remain. Numerous studies for Van Dyck's picture exist, among them one in the Rhode Island School of Design. See Vey, *op. cit.*, Nos. 7–14.

The sketch on the *verso* is a reminiscence of Rubens' *Brazen Serpent* of *c.* 1610, now in the collection of Count Antoine Seilern in London.

81 THE MARRIAGE OF ST. CATHERINE (989)
Pen and brown ink with brown and grey wash over black chalk.
7 1/4×11 in.; 18.2×28 cm.
(The large monogram NL near St. Catherine's left hand has not been explained).
Provenance: N. A. Flinck.
Literature: Vasari Society, III, 1907, 16; *Old Master Drawings*, V, 1930, Pl. 72; H. Vey, *Van Dyck Zeichnungen*, 1962, No. 55, Fig. 75.
Exhibited: Royal Academy, London, 1938, No. 582; Rotterdam, 1948–49, No. 81; Paris, 1949, No. 120; Antwerp and Rotterdam, 1960, No. 29.

A study for the painting in Madrid (Glück, *Kl.d.K.*, 60). Other related drawings are in the Morgan Library, New York; in Bremen; and (formerly) on the market in Berlin (see Vey, *op. cit.*, Nos. 53, 54, 56). The last mentioned is nearest to the painting.

There is another drawing of the same subject at Chatsworth (986), and a copy of the present drawing is in the Louvre (Lugt, *Ec. Flamande*, I, No. 605, Pl. LXI).

82 A GROUP OF SAINTS (991)
SS. Jerome, George, Catherine, Sebastian and others, turning towards left.
Pen and brown wash.
11 5/8×9 1/2 in.; 29.7×24.2 cm.
Provenance: N. A. Flinck.
Literature: Vasari Society, IV, 22; Vey, *Van Dyck Zeichnungen*, 1962, No. 95, Fig. 127.
Exhibited: Antwerp and Rotterdam, 1960, No. 49; Manchester, 1961, No. 73.

A preliminary sketch for an important composition of the Virgin and Child surrounded by Saints, which is further explained on both sides of a sheet in the British Museum, on both sides of another in the Albertina, and on the *recto* of another at Chatsworth (see Horst Vey, *op. cit.*, Nos. 94, 97, 98 and Figs. 126, 128, 131–133). The last has sketches on the *verso* that are connected with a work of Van Dyck's first Antwerp period (before 1622), the *Taking of Christ* at Madrid. The central motive of all the connected drawings is that of St. Jerome kneeling to adore the Child, or to kiss His foot. In the present example this Saint is kneeling on the right; in all the others he is on the left. No painting of this *Sacra Conversazione* is known.

83 HORATIUS COCLES DEFENDING THE BRIDGE OVER THE TIBER (992)
Pen and brown and grey wash.
7 7/8×12 1/8 in.; 20×30.9 cm.
Provenance: N. A. Flinck.
Literature: H. Vey, *Van Dyck Zeichnungen*, 1962, No. 39, Fig. 48.

Exhibited: Antwerp and Rotterdam, 1960, No. 20; Manchester, 1961, No. 74.

A copy is in the Louvre (Lugt, *Ec. Flamande*, I, No. 611, Pl. LXI, with reference to the original at Chatsworth).

84 PORTRAIT OF THE PAINTER GASPAR DE CRAYER (1000)
Black chalk.
9 3/8×7 3/8 in.; 24×18.8 cm.
Provenance: N. A. Flinck.
Literature: Vasari Society, V, 1909, 21; M. Delacre, *Recherches sur le Rôle du Dessein dans l'Iconographie de Van Dyck*, 1932, p. 80; Vey, *Van Dyck Zeichnungen*, No. 260 and Fig. 308.
Exhibited: Royal Academy, London, 1938, No. 583; Rotterdam, 194849, No. 87.

The original study, in reverse, for the engraving by Paul Pontius in the long series of portrait engravings known as the Iconography of Van Dyck (Mauquoy-Hendrickx, 46).

Drawn in Flanders between 1627 and 1635. Gaspar de Crayer (1584–1669) was one of the best of the "history-painters" of his time in the Netherlands. A copy of this drawing is in the Dutuit Collection, Paris, and another is in the Brussels Museum (de Grez Coll.). See Lugt, *Catalogue of the Dutuit Collection*, 1927, No. 30.

There are at Chatsworth eight other original drawings by Van Dyck for the portraits engraved in the Iconography, all from the Flinck Collection.

85 A CLUMP OF TREES BY A COUNTRY ROAD (1004)
Pen and water color.
10 3/4×13 1/4 in.; 27.4×34 cm.
Literature: A. P. Oppé in *Burlington Magazine*, LXXIX, 1941, p. 190; Vey, *Van Dyck Zeichnungen*, 1962, No. 305 and Fig. 357.
Exhibited: Royal Academy, London, 1938, No. 608; Rotterdam, 1949, No. 95; Paris, Bibliothèque Nationale, 1949, No. 134a; Arts Council, London, 1949, No. 28; Genoa, 1955, No. 103; Antwerp and Rotterdam, 1960, No. 119; Manchester, 1961, No. 79.

One of the finest of Van Dyck's landscape watercolors, no doubt done in England (as Paul Oppé suggested) and probably between 1635 and 1640. There are two other similar landscape studies at Chatsworth (Vey, Nos. 306–307.)

Hendrick Goltzius

1558–1616

86 LANDSCAPE WITH PEASANTS BY A HUT (1065)
Pen and dark brown ink.
14×18 3/8 in.; 35.7×46.8 cm.
Signed in monogram and dated A° 1593.
Literature: A. E. Popham in *Burlington Magazine*, 1962, p. 396, Fig. 41.
Exhibited: Manchester, 1965, No. 313.

This very important example of Goltzius' landscape was published for the first time by Mr. Popham in a review of E. K. J. Reznicek's monograph on Goltzius' drawings (1961).

Marten van Heemskerck

(1498–1574)

87 Two drawings on one mount:
A THE ROMAN FORUM FROM BELOW THE CAPITOL LOOKING TOWARDS THE COLOSSEUM (839A)

Pen and brown ink.
5 1/8 × 8 in.; 13 × 20.3 cm.
Literature: H. Egger, *Römische Veduten*, II, 1931, Pl. 9.
Exhibited: Royal Academy, London, 1927, No. 533 (as by Jan Brueghel I).

The drawing, which was probably produced in the early part of Heemskerck's stay in Rome, in 1532 or soon after, shows the remains of the temple of Vespasian on the extreme left, and of the Temple of Saturn extreme right. Egger (*loc. cit.*) draws attention to various interesting topographical features, among them the Campanile and Church of SS. Sergio e Bacco (destroyed 1536) in the left foreground. The column of Phocas, in the center of the composition, is here surrounded by mediaeval secular buildings.

B THE ENTRANCE TO OLD ST. PETER'S AND THE VATICAN PALACE
Pen and brown ink, over light black chalk.
5 1/8 × 8 in.; 13 × 20.3 cm.
Literature: H. Egger, *Römische Veduten*, I, 1911, Pl. 18.
Exhibited: Royal Academy, London, 1927, No. 533 (as by Jan Brueghel I).

The drawing shows almost the same view as a much larger sheet in Vienna by the same artist, drawn between 1532 and 1536 (Egger, *op. cit.*, I, Pl. 17); but is taken from a point a little further away, and more to the right. Egger expressed some doubt as to the authenticity of the Chatsworth drawing, but he knew it only from a photograph, and the attribution is certain. The triple loggia in the center, immediately below the old campanile, is the Loggia della Benedizione begun by Pope Pius II and finished by Alexander VI or Julius II. To the left of this is the entrance to forecourt of the old church, and to the right the entrance to the Vatican Palace. The fountain in the foreground was begun by Innocent VIII, finished by Alexander VI (1502) and removed in the time of Paul V. According to Egger, the detail in the Chatsworth drawing is less accurate than in the large sheet in Vienna. It may be that it was finished in the studio, with the help of the other drawing.

Jan Miel

1599–1663

88 COUNTRYFOLK RESTING AND EATING BY THE ROADSIDE (685)
Pen and water color.
6 3/8 × 18 3/8 in.; 16.1 × 46.9 cm.
Provenance: 2nd Duke of Devonshire.
Exhibited: Royal Academy, London, Drawings by Old Masters, 1953. No. 336.

School of Barend Van Orley

c. 1535–1540

89 WINTER SCENE IN A CASTLE, WITH LADIES AND GENTLEMEN PLAYING CARDS AND DOMINOES
Point of the brush and brown wash over black chalk, heightened with gold, on brown ground.
14 1/2 × 18 1/2 in.; 37.2 × 47.2 cm.

This is one of three drawings of contemporary scenes, all of similar dimensions and in the same elaborate technique, lately discovered by Mr. Thomas Wragg at Chatsworth. The others are: *A Masquerade in the Castle* and a *Winter Scene with Ladies and Gentlemen on the Ice*. They may be projects for a series of important tapestries, comparable to the *Hunts of Maximilian* now in the Louvre (*cf.* Göbel, *Wandteppiche* I–II, 1923, Fig. 71, etc.).

Rembrandt van Rijn

1606–1669

90 ISAAC BLESSING JACOB. on the *verso*, BUST OF A BEARDED MAN IN PROFILE, IN A HIGH CAP (1015)

Pen and brown ink, touched in places with the brush or the feather of the quill pen; the *verso* in black chalk.

6 3/4×7 3/4 in.; 17.6×19.7 cm.

Provenance: N. A. Flinck.

Literature: Benesch, *Rembrandt's Drawings*, V, 891, Fig. 1102 (with earlier literature).

Benesch does not mention the slight sketch on the *verso*. He dates the *recto c.* 1652.

91 DAVID'S CHARGE TO SOLOMON (1016)

Pen and brown wash.

8 5/8×8 1/4 in.; 21.9×20.9 cm.

Provenance: N. A. Flinck.

Literature: Vasari Society, 1st Series, III, 22; Hofstede de Groot, 830; Münz, *Die Graphischen Künste*, N.F. II, 1937, p. 103; Benesch VI (attributed to Rembrandt, A 81).

Exhibited: Royal Academy, London, 1929, No. 613; at the same, 1938, No. 542.

I am not convinced by Benesch's argument in rejecting this drawing from Rembrandt's oeuvre. He says that the drawing is based on the etching of *David in Prayer* of 1652, and therefore must be later than 1650 (why not 1652?). The figure of David in the print is like the figure of Solomon here to the extent that both figures are kneeling and seen from the back, and there is a four-poster bed and a general resemblance in the perspective. All this could be accidental, but in any case it seems at least likely that the etching (which is in reverse) is to some extent a reminiscence of the drawing. Secondly, he considers that it is also derivative from two "mature drawings" by Rembrandt, Benesch 891 (here exhibited as No. 90) and 892 (coll. Lady Melchett) both of *Isaac blessing Jacob*; but in fact these two drawings are much more like one another than either is like the present drawing. Benesch wished to attribute this to Aert de Gelder, and Münz suggested the name of Flinck. I am still inclined to see in it the hand of Rembrandt himself at an appreciably earlier date than in the *Isaac blessing Jacob* (No. 90), perhaps in the early 1640's, as Hofstede de Groot believed.

92 VIEW ON THE AMSTEL, NEAR KOSTVERLOREN, WITH A FENCE IN THE FOREGROUND (1024)

Pen and brown wash, on brown-toned paper with some body color.

5 3/4×8 3/8 in.; 14.5×21.2 cm.

Provenance: N. A. Flinck.

Literature: Benesch, VI, 1266, Fig. 1493 (with other literature).

Exhibited: Royal Academy, London, 1929, No. 607; Royal Academy, 1938, No. 558; Royal Academy, 1953, Drawings by Old Masters, No. 312; Amsterdam and Rotterdam, 1956, No. 153.

Dated by Benesch, *c.* 1651–1652. There is another beautiful drawing at Chatsworth of the same view (No. 1021), made from the same bank a little nearer the Château of Kostverloren, whose tower appears over the treetops; and a third (No. 1025), slighter and more summary in treatment, perhaps drawn at a later season of year, in which more of the buildings in the middle distance are visible.

93 WATER-MEADOWS AT HOUTEWAEL, NEAR THE ST. ANTHONISPOORT (1032)
Pen and brown wash, with some body color.
4 3/4×7 1/8 in.; 12.5×18.2 cm.
Provenance: N. A. Flinck.
Literature: Lugt, *Mit Rembrandt in Amsterdam*, 1920, pp. 133, *ss.*; Benesch, VI, 1261 (with other literature).
Exhibited: Royal Academy, London, 1929, No. 608; Stockholm, 1956.

On the back is a pen sketch of cottages with figures on the road to Houtewael—the same view, from further away, appears in a drawing at Rotterdam (Benesch, 1262). The village was identified by Mr. Lugt (*loc. cit.*), who adds the information that a friend of Rembrandt's, Reynier Engelen or Ingels, whom he had portrayed as a Serjeant in the *Night Watch* of 1642, was Pastor at Houtewael.

Dated by Benesch *c.* 1651.

94 VIEW ON THE BULLEWIJK, LOOKING TOWARDS OUDERKERK, WITH A ROWING BOAT (1033)
Pen and brown wash, touched with body color.
5 1/4×7 7/8 in.; 13.3×20 cm.
Provenance: N. A. Flinck.
Literature: Benesch, VI, 1232 (with other literature).
Exhibited: Royal Academy, London, 1929, No. 604; Royal Academy, 1938, No. 544; Stockholm, 1956.

One of the most beautiful and famous of all Rembrandt's landscape drawings, dated by Benesch *c.* 1650. The view was identified by Mr. F. Lugt (*Mit Rembrandt in Amsterdam*, 1920, p. 125 and Pl. 78).

95 A VILLAGE INN BY THE ROADSIDE (1036)
Pen and brown ink, on buff-grey prepared paper.
3 7/8×8 7/8 in.; 10×22.6 cm.
Provenance: N. A. Flinck.
Literature: Benesch, VI, 1314 (with other literature).

Dated by Benesch *c.* 1652–1653.

96 TWO THATCHED COTTAGES (1038)
Pen and brown ink, with some body color.
5 3/8×7 7/8 in.; 13.7×20 cm.
Literature: Vasari Society, 1st Series, III, 24; Benesch, IV, 796 (with earlier literature).
Exhibited: Royal Academy, London, 1929, No. 603.

Dated by Benesch *c.* 1640–1641.

97 VIEW OF SLOTEN (1039)
Pen and brown wash, with some body color on brown-toned paper.
3 3/4×7 in.; 9.6×18 cm.
Provenance: N. A. Flinck.
Literature: Lugt, *Mit Rembrandt in Am-*

sterdam, 1920, p. 155; Benesch, VI, 1237 (with other literature).
Exhibited: Royal Academy, London, 1929, No. 610; Stockholm, 1956.

Dated by Benesch *c.* 1650.

Sir Peter Paul Rubens

1577–1640

98 SKETCHES FOR A WOLF-HUNT (982)
Black and red chalk and water color.
9 5/8×14 1/8 in.; 24.7×36 cm.
Provenance: N. A. Flinck.

The drawing, including the elaborate water color, is of high quality throughout, but its close correspondence with Rubens' painting, now in the Metropolitan Museum, suggests a derivation from the picture by a very good hand (Van Dyck?) rather than a study for it. A good replica of the painting is in the Methuen Collection at Corsham (Borenius, Cat., 1939, No. 128).

99 A FALLEN TREE LYING BY A POOL (985)
Black chalk, with slight touches of water color.
7 1/4×12 1/8 in.; 18.4×30.9 cm.
Literature: Clare Stuart-Wortley in *Old Master Drawings*, IX, Dec. 1936, Pl. 45: Glück, *Die Landschaften von P. P. Rubens*, 1945, pp. 29 and 61, Fig. 7; Held, *Rubens, Selected Drawings*, 1959, No. 132, Pl. 144; Burchard and d'Hulst, *Rubens Drawings*, 1963, No. 103.
Exhibited: Rotterdam, 1948–49, No. 130; Paris, 1949, No. 112; Arts Council, London, 1949, No. 47; Brussels, 1953, No. 48; Antwerp, 1956, No. 106.

Mr. Frits Lugt has observed that the same fallen tree, from a different point of view, seems to be the subject of a magnificent drawing in pen and wash in the Louvre (Cat., *Ec. flamande*, II, 1949, No. 1034).

It seems likely that the Chatsworth drawing dates from *c.* 1617–1619, and that it was used about ten years later for the *Landscape with Ulysses and Nausicaa*, painted *c.* 1627–1630, now in Florence (Oldenbourg, *Kl.d.K.* 354).

100 FOUR NUDE FEMALE FIGURES ROUND A BASIN (1013)
Pen and brown ink. There are some notes, apparently accounts, in black chalk on the *verso*.
4 1/2×8 1/2 in.; 11.4×21.6 cm.
Literature: Burchard and d'Hulst, *Rubens Drawings*, 1963, pp. 25–26.
Exhibited: Royal Academy, London, 1953–1954, No. 514; Antwerp, 1956, No. 7.

A beautiful example of Rubens' penmanship, first recognized by the late Ludwig Burchard. Dr. Wolfgang Burchard, his son, has since drawn attention to the fact that this and a drawing in the British Museum of *Three Nymphs undressing* (Hind, II, No. 26, as Van Dyck) derive from two of a set of sixteen plaquettes, illustrating scenes from Ovid's *Metamorphoses*, modelled and cast by the Flemish sculptor Jacob Cornelisz Cobbe. Cobbe was chief assistant to Guglielmo della Porta (d. 1577), and himself died in Rome at an advanced age in 1615. A complete set of these plaquettes, in bronze, is in Vienna. The Chatsworth sheet reproduces details of the oval plaquette, *Midas celebrating the Arrival of Silenus* (Ovid, *Met.* IX, 85–96). Both drawings were no doubt done in Rome, 1600–1608.

Roelant Savery

1576–1639

101 A DREDGER ON A WIDE RIVER (840)
Pen and brown wash, over black chalk on several pieces of paper, joined.
7½×12⅞ in.; 19×33 cm.
Literature: Vasari Society, 1st Series, VII, 18; Tolnai, *Die Zeichnungen Pieter Bruegels*, 1925, No. 49; Michel, *Bruegel*, 1931, p. 102.
Exhibited: Royal Academy, London, 1927, No. 524 (as by Pieter Bruegel I); Brussels, 1935, No. 484.

Formerly attributed to the elder Bruegel, but almost certainly by Savery.

German and Swiss

Bavarian School

c. 1530

102 A BATTLE BY A BRIDGE OVER A WIDE RIVER ISSUING FROM A LAKE (934)
Pen and ink on dark brown ground, heightened with white.
11×16¾ in.; 28×42.9 cm.
Provenance: N. A. Flinck.
Literature: Campbell Dodgson in Vasari Society, 1st Series, VII, 26.

Formerly attributed to Altdorfer, but certainly not by him, though reminiscent of Altdorfer's famous painting, now in Munich, of *The Battle of Arbela*, as Campbell Dodgson (*loc. cit.*) remarked. According to Dodgson, Ernst Buchner suggested an attribution to Ruprecht Heller, by whom there is a signed painting of the *Battle of Pavia* at Stockholm.

The drawing is a typical example of the "manner" of the so-called Danube School, under the inspiration of Altdorfer and Wolf Huber, in the first half of the XVI century.

German (?) School

Early XVI century

103 AN OLD MAN, THREE-QUARTER LENGTH, GESTICULATING (642C)
Pen and brown ink, with some corrections in body color, and some black chalk.
7¾×5½ in.; 19.8×14 cm.
Provenance: P. H. Lankrink.

The presence of the Lankrink mark (P. H. Lankrink, 1628–1692) practically rules out the old attribution to Ghezzi (P. L. Ghezzi, 1674–1755), but in any case it is obvious that this excellent drawing is of much earlier date. Mr. Popham suggests that it may be by Quentin Massys, and indeed the grotesque type, reminiscent of Leonardo's caricatures, would be characteristic of Massys; but there are no comparable drawings by him, and the loose penwork is very like Dürer's in his more summary sketches of early date. A similar grotesque type appears in Dürer's painting of *Christ among the Doctors*, dated 1506, in the Barberini Collection, Rome.

Swiss School, c. 1520 extensively reworked by Rubens

104 A LADY HOLDING A SHIELD: A DESIGN FOR GLASS (838)
The original in pen and indian ink;

Rubens' additions in pen and brown wash, with white oil color.
10 1/4 × 8 1/4 in.; 26 × 21 cm.
Provenance: N. A. Flinck.
Literature: Vasari Society, 1st Series, v, 29 (as School of Holbein); J. Held, *Rubens, Selected Drawings*, 1959, No. 168, Pl. 178 and Fig. 44 (with other literature).

What remains visible of the original drawing (architecture, hat, right sleeve, underskirt and foot) seems to me nearer in style to Hans Holbein the Younger, in his bold, early designs for glass-painting, than to any of the other artists whose names have been suggested. Dr. E. Schilling proposed that of Daniel Hopfer.

Rubens has transformed the face, the hands and most of the dress. The shield (with the arms visible in the infra-red photograph reproduced by Held, *loc. cit.*) was originally drawn in front of the figure; Rubens has carried the full drapery of the skirt across it, so that it appears to be held (rather awkwardly) half behind the lady's back.

Hans Baldung Grien (?)

1484/5–1545(?)

105 Two sheets from a sketchbook, on one mount: (832)

A A PEASANT SEATED, AND A HOUSE AMONG TREES IN A LANDSCAPE

B AN EXECUTIONER

Silverpoint on grey prepared ground.
6 3/8 × 4 3/8 in.; 16.4 × 11.2 cm. (both)

These drawings, once attributed to Lucas van Leyden, seem to me certainly by the same hand, and perhaps from the same sketchbook, as three other small sheets at Chatsworth, with silverpoint drawings on both sides, which were published by Campbell Dodgson in the Vasari Society, 2nd Series, VI, 1925, Nos. 13–16: two of them studies of *Peasants' Heads*, and one with a *Woman's Profile* on the *recto* and a *Study of a Goat* on the *verso* (99 × 126 mm.)

Mr. Dodgson (who did not connect the present drawings with the three others) pointed out that the old attribution of the *Goat* to Pisanello was as absurd as the still older attribution of all three to Leonardo; and rightly maintained that they are of the German School of the early XVI century. All five sheets, including those now exhibited, seem to me so close in style and subject to the later drawings in the so-called sketchbook of Baldung at Carlsruhe (which in fact contains drawings, in the same technique as these, of various dates, and to which certain drawings in Copenhagen seem to belong) that I venture to propose this attribution. For the related drawings, see Carl Koch, *Hans Baldungs Zeichnungen*, 1941, pls. 160–252.

Jörg Breu (the younger)

c. 1510–1547

106 A PARTY IN THE GROUNDS OF A MOATED CASTLE (664)

Pen and brown wash.
10 7/8 × 16 1/8 in.; 27.8 × 41.4 cm.
Inscribed by the artist (lower right): *das erst stueck*, and dated (above, left center) 1534.
Literature: Campbell Dodgson in Vasari Society, 1st Series, VIII, 31; H. Leporini, *Die Stilentwicklung*, 1925, No. 72; H. Röttinger in Vienna *Jahrbuch*, XXVIII, p. 31 *ss.*
Exhibited: Royal Academy, London,

Drawings by Old Masters, 1953, No. 245.

According to Campbell Dodgson (*loc. cit.*), the inscription (meaning "the first piece") implies that an extension of the composition (no doubt to the right) will follow to complete the design. It is probably a sketch for a large woodcut. Very similar buildings and figures occur in *The Rich Man and Lazarus* of 1535 (Geisberg, *Der deutsche Einblatt-Holzschnitt in der ersten Hälfte des XVI Jahrhunderts*, 1930, No. 397), and in the *Venetian Banquet* (on three blocks, Geisberg, 402–404).

The scene is an amusing mixture of Venetian and German Renaissance elements.

Albrecht Dürer

1471–1528

107 THE VIRGIN AND CHILD WITH THE INFANT ST. JOHN (830)
Pen and brown ink.
11 1/4×8 1/8 in.; 28.6×20.5 cm.
Signed (?) with the monogram lower right.
Provenance: 2nd Duke of Devonshire.
Literature: Winkler, *Dürers Zeichnungen*, III, 1938, No. 538 (with other literature).
Exhibited: Arts Council, London, 1949, No. 51.

Closely related in style and type of the Virgin to the beautiful woodcut of 1518, *The Virgin with the many Angels* (Bartsch 101), and almost certainly of that date.

Winkler (*loc. cit.*) considered that the monogram may have been added by another hand.

Hans Rottenhammer

1564–1625

108 THE RAISING OF LAZARUS (692)
Pen and brown wash, heightened with white, on buff ground.
10 3/8×9 in.; 26.4×23 cm.
Provenance: Sir Peter Lely; 2nd Duke of Devonshire.

A fine, pictorially finished example of Rottenhammer, who was in Venice 1595–1606 and was greatly influenced by Tintoretto and Paolo Veronese. Both influences are evident here—that of Tintoretto in the group on the right, and that of Veronese in the woman (Martha or Mary) kneeling in the foreground.

French

Jacques Callot

1592–1635

109 LOUIS DE LORRAINE-GUISE, PRINCE DE PHALSBURG, ON HORSEBACK (696)
Black chalk and brown wash, pricked for transfer.
9 3/4×13 1/8 in.; 24.7×33.3 cm.
Provenance: 2nd Duke of Devonshire.
Literature: Daniel Ternois, *Jacques Callot, Oeuvre Dessiné*, 1961, No. 789.
Exhibited: Royal Academy, London, 1938, No. 495; at the same, 1953, No. 366.

This important drawing, not belonging to the Chatsworth Album (see Nos. 111–115), is the preliminary study in reverse for Callot's etching, Lieure 505, of 1624, in which the figure of the Prince is changed, so that the baton should not appear in his left hand when the composition was reversed in printing. A later preparatory drawing, followed more exactly in the etching, is in the British Museum (Ternois, 790), and a study for the armor, gauntlet and baton is in the Hermitage (Album Julienne, No. 1483, Ternois, 791). Ternois must be wrong in identifying the Chatsworth drawing with that in the Paignon-Dijonval sale of 1810, No. 2525, afterwards the property of Robert Dumesnil in 1853, since it bears the mark of the 2nd Duke of Devonshire (d. 1729) which was certainly not used later than the mid-XVIII century.

110 LANDSCAPE WITH BATHERS (947)

Black chalk with brown wash, with some body color, indented with the stylus.

7 3/8×13 1/8 in.; 18.7×33.5 cm.

Provenance: 2nd Duke of Devonshire.

Literature: Daniel Ternois, *Jacques Callot, Oeuvre Dessiné*, 1961, No. 431.

Exhibited: Brussels and Rotterdam, 1949; Manchester, 1965, No. 282.

Not belonging to the Chatsworth album (see Nos. 111–115). It was once attributed to Claude, but as M. Ternois has pointed out, it is the first preliminary, on a large scale, for the landscape etched by Callot as one of the ten *Paysages Italiens* (Lieure 270), the immediate model for which was a pen drawing in the Chatsworth album (Ternois, 1961, No. 433). Another preliminary drawing in black chalk and wash is in the Louvre (Ternois, 432).

There are some reminiscences of Florence (Palazzo Vecchio, etc.) in the background of the present drawing, which are omitted in the two others and in the print, but it would be wrong to describe it (as in the Manchester catalogue of 1965) as a scene on the Arno. The drawing must have been done in Florence 1618–1620, and etched after the artist's return to Nancy.

111–114 NINE DRAWINGS FOR *LA GRANDE PASSION*

All in brush and brown wash over black chalk.

4×8 1/2 in.; 10.0×21.5 cm.

Provenance: Mariette (Sale Catalogue, ed. Basan 1775, No. 1185).

Literature: A. F. Blunt in catalogue of Royal Academy Exhibition, *Landscape in French Art*, 1949, No. 565; D. Ternois, *Jacques Callot, Oeuvre Dessiné*, 1961, pp. 98–99.

From the series of thirteen original studies for etchings that form part of the now celebrated Chatsworth album of more than 140 drawings and nearly twice as many etchings by the master. The album, whose pedigree was first studied by Sir Anthony Blunt and was later corrected by M. Daniel Ternois (see above), was exhibited intact at the Royal Academy 1949–1950. The main part of the drawings belonged to Israel Silvestre (1621–1691); but the *Passion* drawings, according to M. Ternois, were in Paris already in 1684 (Félibien, ed. 1775, pp. 376–377), belonged to Mariette, and must have been inserted in the album later. For the first time permission has been given for the four pages containing these nine drawings, and those containing No. 115 A and B, to be removed from the Chatsworth album for the purpose of the present exhibition. Only seven of the thirteen subjects were etched by Callot in the series known as *La Grande Passion* (Lieure, 281–287). Single figure studies for the series are in the Album

Julienne at Leningrad and the Album Mariette in the Louvre (Ternois, Nos. 593–662).

111 A THE TAKING OF CHRIST (Ternois, No. 577)

This drawing, exceedingly dramatic in its effect of torchlight, was not etched. M. Ternois may be right in supposing that Callot was discouraged from completing the etched series by the difficulty of maintaining this effect in the reproductive medium.

B CHRIST BEFORE PILATE (Ternois, No. 577) Not etched.

112 A ECCE HOMO (Ternois, No. 583)

Study in reverse for the etching, Lieure 285, which has many more figures. Another preliminary drawing, earlier than this, is in the Hermitage (Ternois, 582).

B CHRIST CROWNED WITH THORNS (Ternois, No. 580)

Study in reverse for the etching, Lieure 284, which shows considerable variations.

113 A THE PROCESSION TO CALVARY (Ternois, No. 585)

Study in reverse for the etching, Lieure 286, in which more figures are added. A first idea for this composition belongs to Monsieur A. Strolin, Paris (T. 584).

B CHRIST NAILED TO THE CROSS (Ternois, No. 586)

Study in reverse for the etching, Lieure 287, which according to Mariette is by Silvestre, except for some of the principal figures which are by Callot himself. The rough vigor of the executioners and the reactions of the bystanders are realized with extraordinary insight and imagination.

114 A CALVARY (Ternois, No. 587)
Not etched.

B THE DESCENT FROM THE CROSS (Ternois, No. 588)
Not etched.

C THE RESURRECTION (Ternois, No. 589) Not etched.

115 A A WOMAN HOLDING A SPINDLE (Ternois, No. 1255)
Black chalk.
6 1/8×3 5/8 in.; 15.7×9.3 cm.
Etched in reverse by I. Henriet (Meaume 1211).

B A WOMAN WITH A BASKET ON HER ARM (Ternois, No. 1256)
Black chalk, indented for transfer with the stylus.
6 1/8×3 5/8 in.; 15.7×9.3 cm.
Etched in reverse by I. Henriet (Meaume 1212).

There are nineteen of these excellent studies in black chalk, called by Ternois *Bourgeoises dans différentes attitudes*, in the Chatsworth album, and also a considerable number of pen copies, no doubt done by Henriet for the etched series, which is incomplete. See Ternois, *loc. cit.*

Claude Gellée, called Le Lorrain

1600–1682

116 ST. JOHN THE BAPTIST PREACHING IN A ROCKY LANDSCAPE (863)
Brush and brown wash, over black chalk, on pinkish ground.
7 1/2×9 7/8 in.; 19.2×25.2 cm.
Literature: M. Chiarini, *Claudio Lorenese, Disegni*, Florence, 1968, No. 49.

The drawing, which is exceptional in the large scale of the figures, has not been exhibited in recent years. It was formerly attributed to Poussin, then to Grimaldi, but is certainly by Claude as was pointed out by Dr. Chiarini.

117 LANDSCAPE WITH CHRIST PREACHING THE SERMON ON THE MOUNT (939)
Pen and grey wash.
11 1/2×17 3/8 in.; 29.2×44.4 cm.
Provenance: 2nd Duke of Devonshire.
Exhibited: Royal Academy, London, 1949–1950, No. 494.

This very large and splendid drawing, itself engraved by Earlom in *Liber Veritatis*, III, 100, is more successful in composition than the great painting of the same subject, formerly belonging to the Duke of Westminster, and now in the Frick Collection, New York.

The painting (*Liber Veritatis*, 138) was done in 1656 for François Bosquet, Bishop of Montpellier. In it the mount on which Christ is preaching is a much more dominating feature of the landscape.

118 WOODED LANDSCAPE WITH JUPITER AND CALLISTO (945)
Pen and brown and grey wash, with body color over black chalk.
10 1/8×13 1/8 in.; 25.7×33.5 cm.
Signed lower right: CLAUDIO INVFEC.
Provenance: 2nd Duke of Devonshire.
Exhibited: Royal Academy, London, 1949–1950, No. 490.

This beautiful drawing was engraved in the *Liber Veritatis*, Earlom, III, 90. The subject was recently identified by Mr. Michael Kitson.

Nicolas Poussin

1594–1665

119 APOLLO AND DAPHNE (859)
Pen and brown ink.
7 3/4×6 3/4 in.; 19.8×17.1 cm.
Provenance: Sir Peter Lely; 2nd Duke of Devonshire.
Literature: W. Friedländer and A. F. Blunt, *The Drawings of Nicolas Poussin*, III, 1953, p. 17, No. 172.
Exhibited: Manchester, 1961, No. 88.

Connected by Friedländer and Blunt with a painting now lost but described in some detail by Bellori. Datable *c.* 1635. The painting of *Pan and Syrinx* at Dresden (*c.* 1637) seems to echo the general design and repeats some details.

120 THE RAPE OF THE SABINES (861)
Pen and brown wash.
6 1/2×8 7/8 in.; 16.4×22.5 cm.
Provenance: 2nd Duke of Devonshire.
Literature: W. Friedländer (with Anthony Blunt and R. Wittkower), *The Drawings of Nicolas Poussin*, II, 1949, No. 114.
Exhibited: Paris, 1960, No. 149.

There are two paintings of this subject by Poussin, one in the Louvre, painted for Cardinal Omodei (*c.* 1633–1635), the other now in the Metropolitan Museum, New York. The Chatsworth drawing is a study for the Louvre version. Another drawing is in the Uffizi (Friedländer, *op. cit.*, No. 115), with variations, particularly on the right.

Illustrations

1. ANONYMOUS NORTH ITALIAN: A Peacock

4. ANONYMOUS ITALIAN: A Hawfinch, with another study of the underside of the same bird

5. ANONYMOUS ITALIAN: A Duck

2. ANONYMOUS NORTH ITALIAN: A Duck in Flight

3. ANONYMOUS VENETIAN SCHOOLS: Periwinkles and Violets

6. ANONYMOUS ITALIAN: A Monkey Seated, to right

7. ANONYMOUS VENETIAN SCHOOL: The Execution of a Saint

8. ANONYMOUS FLORENTINE SCHOOL: A page from Vasari's *Libro di Disegni*
Recto: PILATE WASHING HIS HANDS

9. NORTH ITALIAN: Bust Portrait of a Man in Profile to left

10. ANONYMOUS EMILIAN (?) SCHOOL: Head of a Bearded Man, looking up to right

11. NICCOLÒ DELL'ABBATE: The Holy Family with St. Elizabeth and the Infant St. John: The Angel Appearing to the Shepherds in the Background

12. FRANCESCO ALBANI: An Allegory: Hercules as Atlas Supporting the Globe, with Mercury and Apollo

8. ANONYMOUS FLORENTINE SCHOOL: A page from Vasari's *Libro di Disegni*
Verso: CHRIST CARRYING THE CROSS

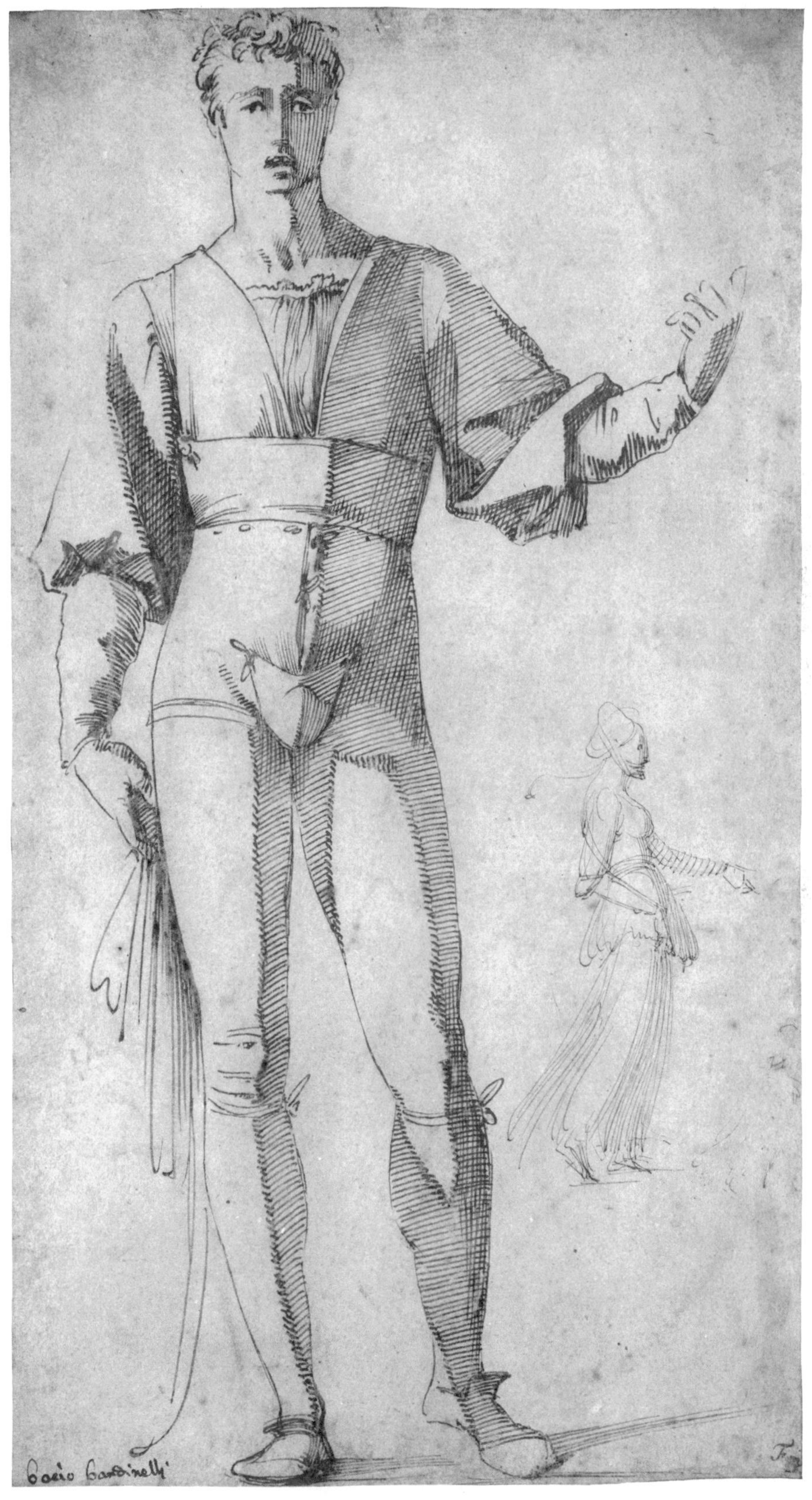

13. BACCIO BANDINELLI: Study of a Young Man in Contemporary Dress

14. BACCIO BANDINELLI: Three Sages Holding Tablets, at an Antique Altar

15. FEDERICO BAROCCI: Head of a Boy

16. FEDERICO BAROCCI: The Assumption of the Virgin

17. FEDERICO BAROCCI: The Visitation

17. Verso. FEDERICO BAROCCI: Study of the Virgin

18a. BONIFACIO DE'PITATI: The Virgin and Child with St. Roch and The Infant St. John the Baptist

18b. BONIFACIO DE'PITATI: Variant of 18a

19. LUCA CAMBIASO: The Holy Family in the Carpenter's Shop

20. DOMENICO CAMPAGNOLA: Christ and St. Peter Walking on the Water

21. SIMONE CANTARINI: Diana and Actaeon

22. ANNIBALE CARRACCI: Pan and Diana

23. ANNIBALE CARRACCI: The Madonna of Bologna

24. ANNIBALE CARRACCI: Christ Crowned with Thorns

25. ANNIBALE CARRACCI: A Woman Seated in a Room

26. ANNIBALE CARRACCI: The Virgin and Child

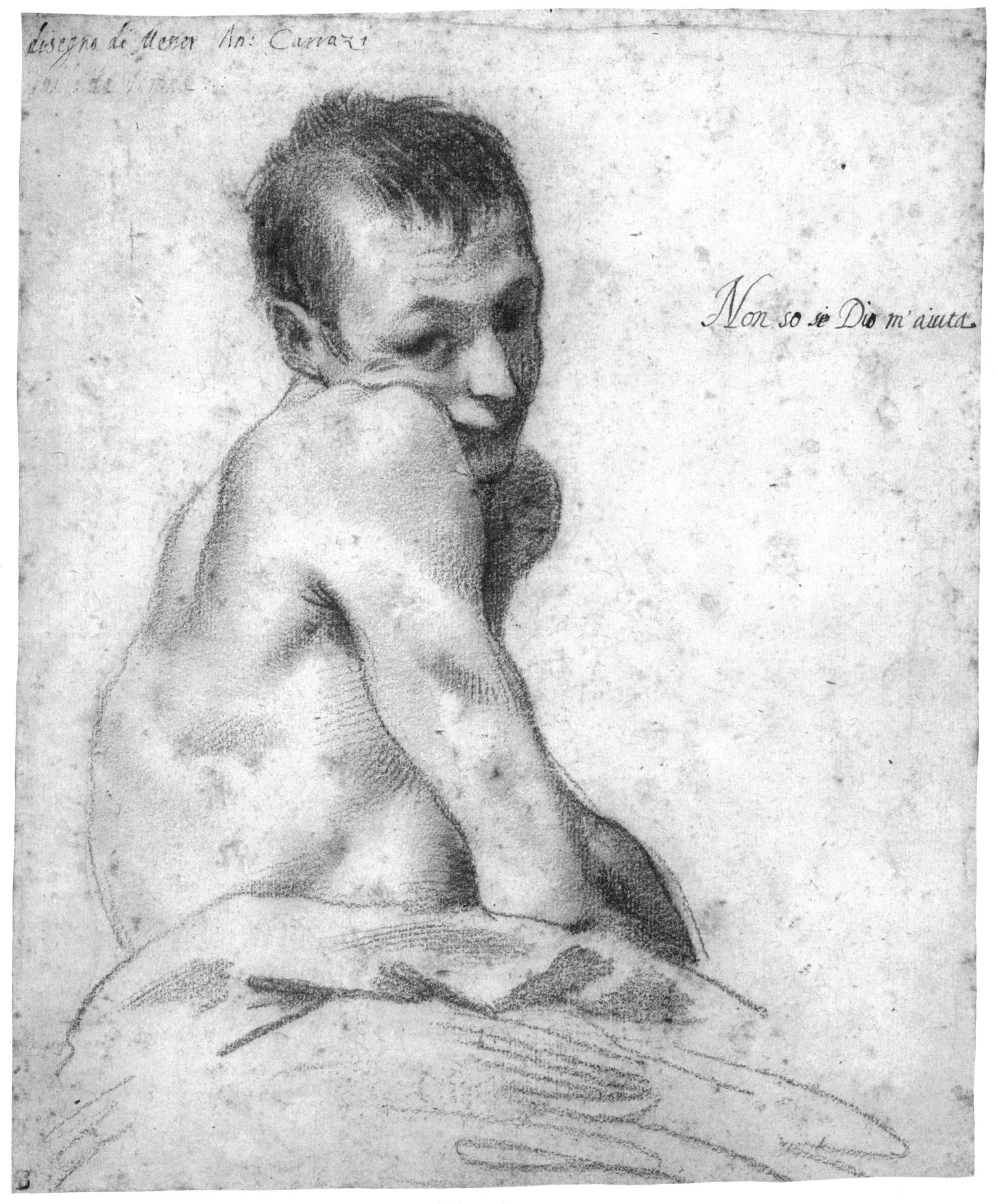

27. ANNIBALE CARRACCI: A Cripple Boy, Half-length

28. ANNIBALE CARRACCI: Landscape with Gypsies

29. GIOVANNI BENEDETTO CASTIGLIONE: A Burial

30. GIOVANNI BENEDETTO CASTIGLIONE: Et in Arcadia Ego

31. GIUSEPPE CESARI, called CAVALIERE D'ARPINO: An Allegorical Design, with the Arms of the Medici

32. CARLO DOLCI: Portrait of the Artist's Shoemaker

33a. FILIPPINO LIPPI: Study of a Young Man Wearing a Short Coat

33b. FILIPPINO LIPPI: Two Studies of a Heavily Draped Figure

34. STUDIO OF FILIPPINO LIPPI: A page from Vasari's *Libro di Disegni*
a. A Nude Man Seated on the Ground
b. A Nude Man in the Attitude of a Beggar; and A Nude Man in Violent Action

35. GIULIO PIPPI, called GIULIO ROMANO: Study for the Marriage Feast of Cupid and Psyche

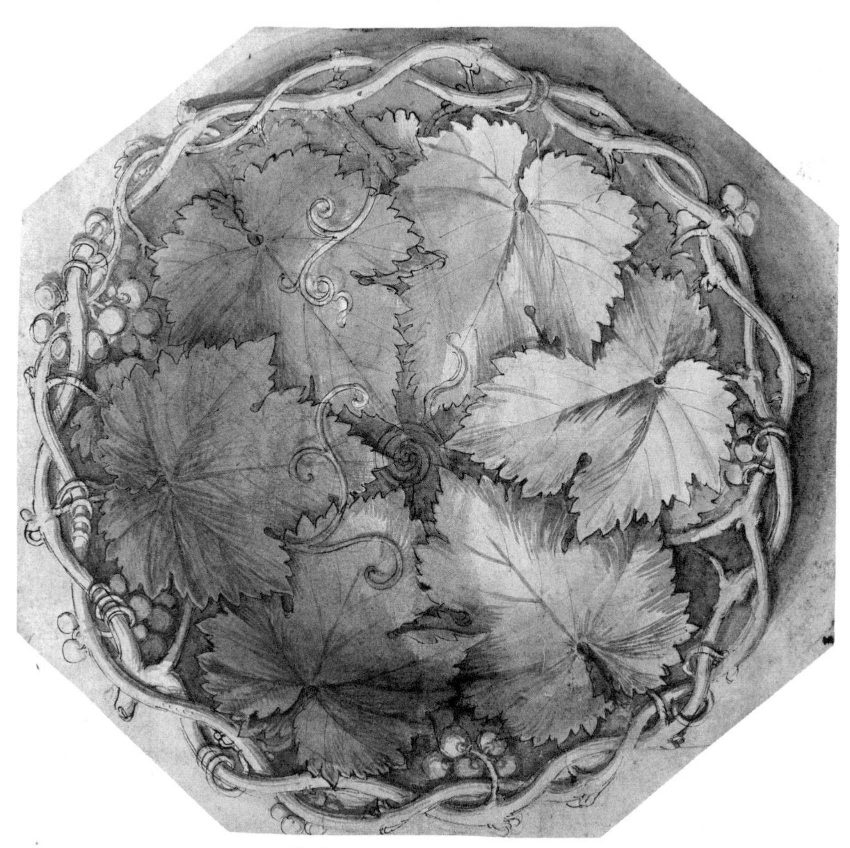

36. GIULIO PIPPI, called GIULIO ROMANO: Design for a Fruit Dish

37. GIULIO PIPPI, called GIULIO ROMANO: The Erotes of Philostratus

38. GIOVANNI FRANCESCO BARBIERI, called GUERCINO: The Madonna del Carmine Offering the Scapula to S. Alberto

39. GIOVANNI FRANCESCO BARBIERI, called GUERCINO: Landscape with a Funeral Procession

40. GIOVANNI FRANCESCO BARBIERI, called GUERCINO: Landscape with a Horseman and Two Soldiers by a River

41. ATTRIBUTED TO LATTANZIO DA RIMINI: St. Mark Preaching

42. CARLO MARATTI: Design for a Large Title-Page, with an Allegorical Figure of the Catholic Church, and Justice Seated Beside Her

43. CARLO MARATTI: Padre Sebastiano Resta Examining a Volume of Drawings

44. PIERFRANCESCO MOLA: Iris Sent by Juno to Turnus

45. JACOPO PALMA, called PALMA GIOVANE: The Translation of the Body of St. Lucy to Venice by the Doge Enrico Dandolo

47. FRANCESCO MAZZUOLA, called IL PARMIGIANINO: A Shepherd Asleep, Under a Tree

46. JACOPO PALMA, called PALMA GIOVANE: Three Heads, Inscribed as Portraits of the Painters Jacopo Bassano, Paolo Veronese, and Pietre Malombra

48. FRANCESCO MAZZUOLA, called IL PARMIGIANINO: Head of a Boy in Profile To Right

49. FRANCESCO MAZZUOLA, called IL PARMIGIANINO: The Virgin and Child, Half-Length

50. FRANCESCO MAZZUOLA, called IL PARMIGIANINO: A Group of Putti, with Trees Below

51. FRANCESCO MAZZUOLA, called IL PARMIGIANINO: Bust of a Bearded Man in Profile To Left

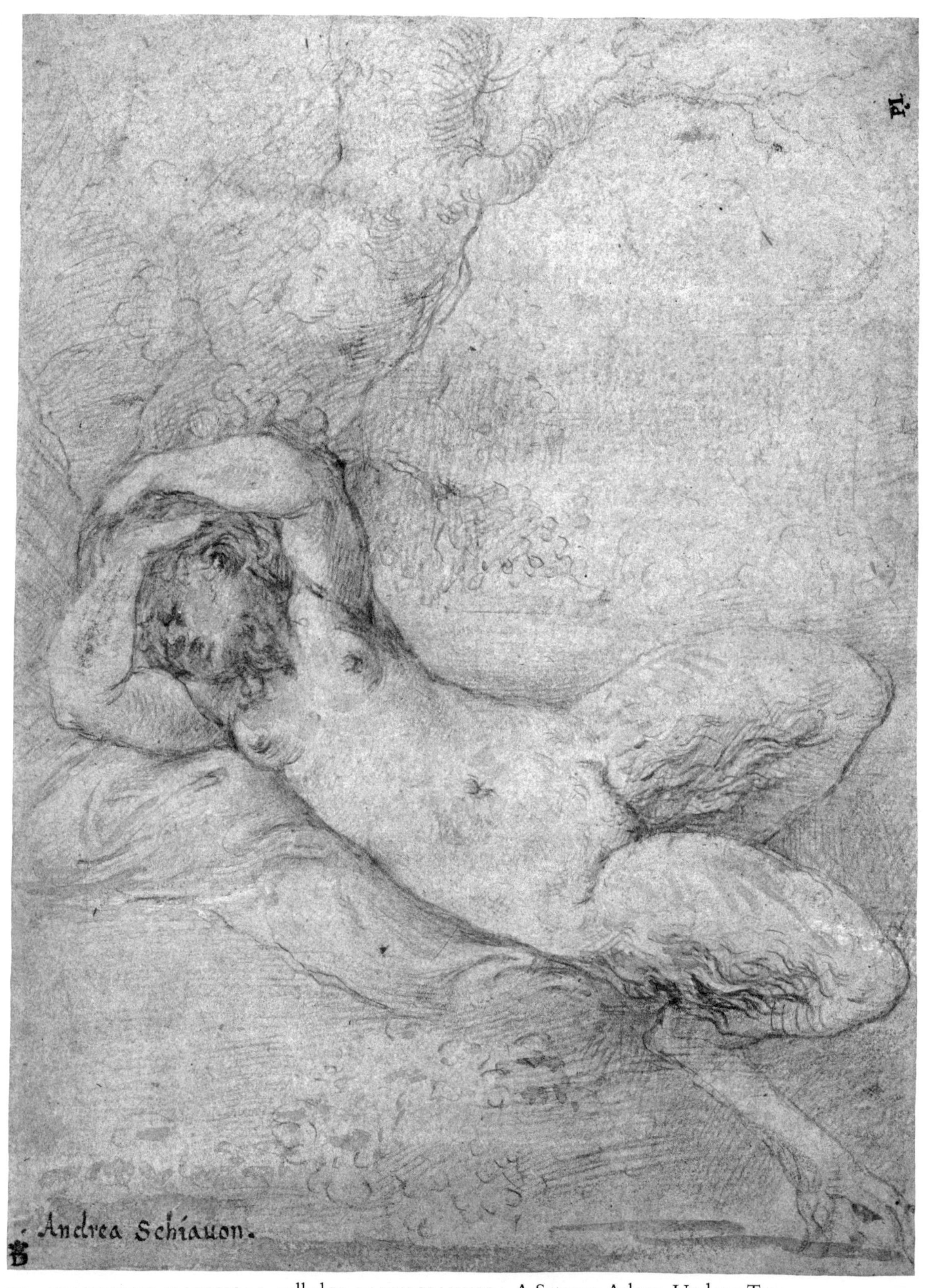

52. FRANCESCO MAZZUOLA, called IL PARMIGIANINO: A Satyress Asleep, Under a Tree

53. PIETRO BUONACCORSI, called PERINO DEL VAGA: Study for an Altarpiece—The Virgin and Child Enthroned, with SS. Gregory (?) and James (?), and a Family of Donors

54. PIETRO BUONACCORSI, called PERINO DEL VAGA: The Holy Family with St. Peter Introducing a Donor

55. RAPHAEL: Mercury and Psyche

56. RAPHAEL: Study of One of the Marble Horses of the Quirinal

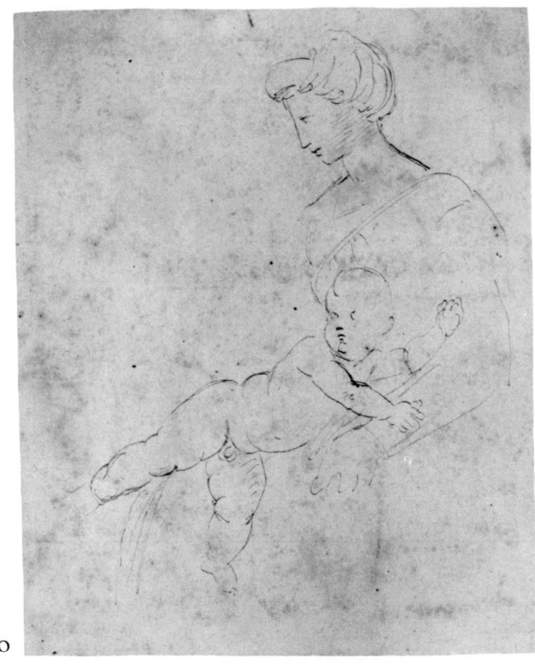

57. Verso. RAPHAEL:
A Madonna and Child after Michelangelo

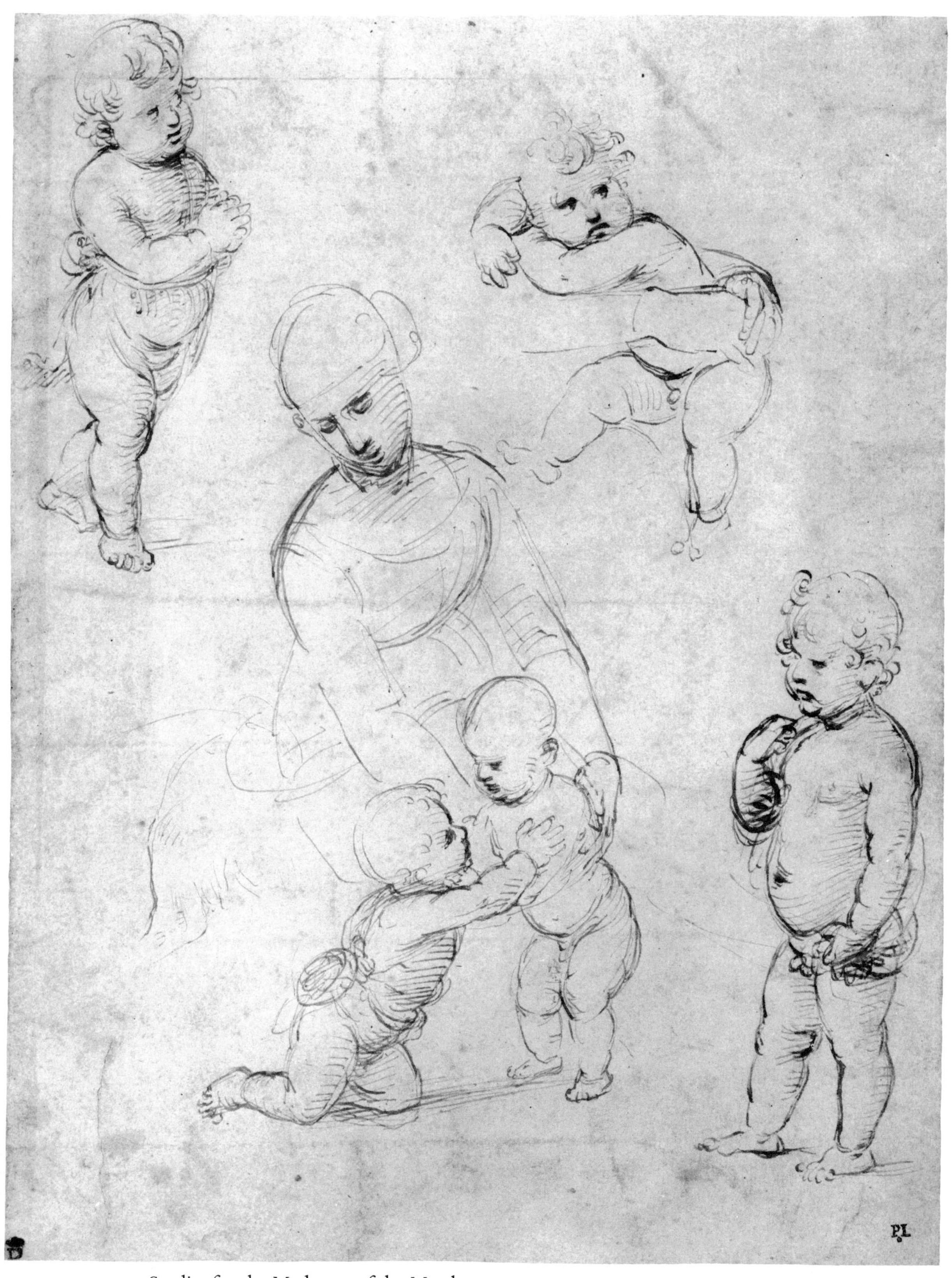

57. RAPHAEL: Studies for the Madonna of the Meadow

58. RAPHAEL: Study for the Transfiguration, with Nude Figures

59. SCHOOL OF RAPHAEL (G. F. Penni?): Constantine, Addressing His Troops, Startled by the Vision of the Cross in the Sky

60. GIROLAMO ROMANINO: Study of an Executioner

61. ROMANINO: A Family Seated Round a Table

62. BARTOLOMEO SCHEDONI: A Mother and Child

63. FRANCISCO SOLIMENA: Heliodorus Driven from the Temple

64. FRANCISCO SOLIMENA: The Virgin and Child in the Clouds, Crowned by an Angel, with SS. Monica, Augustine and Dominic, and the Souls in Purgatory Below

65. PARRI SPINELLI: Christ and the Woman Taken in Adultery

65. Verso. PARRI SPINELLI: Pilgrims at a Shrine

66. PIETRO TESTA: An Allegory of the Cross

67. DOMENICO TINTORETTO: The Virgin and Child in the Clouds Presenting a Rosary to a Saint; A Bishop and Other Figures Below

68. ATTRIBUTED TO TITIAN: Pastoral Landscape with a Nude Woman on the Right, Her Head Enveloped in a Cloak

69. FRANCESCO VANNI: The Madonna Immacolata, with Five Saints

71. VANNI (?): The Holy Family

70. FRANCESCO VANNI: A Woman, Half-length, and Other Studies

72. GIORGIO VASARI: Design for a Ceiling

73. PAOLO CALIARI, called VERONESE: A Political Allegory

74. FEDERICO ZUCCARO: The Coronation of the Virgin, with SS. Lawrence, Damasus, Peter and Paul in the Foreground, and the Martyrdom of St. Lawrence in the Background

75. FEDERICO ZUCCARO: Portrait of an Old Lady, Half-length

76. FEDERICO ZUCCARO: Portrait of a Bearded Man, Half-length

77. TADDEO ZUCCARO: A Group of Horses and Men, Facing Right

78. PAUL BRILL: Roman Landscape with Ruined Mediaeval Buildings Overgrown by Trees

79. SIR ANTHONY VAN DYCK: A Study of Cows

80. SIR ANTHONY VAN DYCK: Christ Carrying the Cross

81. SIR ANTHONY VAN DYCK: The Marriage of St. Catherine

80. Verso: SIR ANTHONY VAN DYCK:
A Sketch of the Brazen Serpent

82. SIR ANTHONY VAN DYCK: A Group of Saints

84. SIR ANTHONY VAN DYCK: Portrait of the Painter Gaspar de Crayer

83. SIR ANTHONY VAN DYCK: Horatius Cocles Defending the Bridge Over the Tiber

85. SIR ANTHONY VAN DYCK: A Clump of Trees by a Country Road

86. HENDRICK GOLTZIUS: Landscape with Peasants by a Hut

87a. MARTEN VAN HEEMSKERCK: The Roman Forum From Below the Capitol Looking Towards the Colosseum

87b. MARTEN VAN HEEMSKERCK: The Entrance to Old St. Peter's and the Vatican Palace

88. JAN MIEL: Countryfolk Resting and Eating by the Roadside

89. SCHOOL OF BAREND VAN ORLEY: Winter Scene in a Castle, with Ladies and Gentlemen Playing Cards and Dominoes

90. REMBRANDT VAN RIJN: Isaac Blessing Jacob

92. REMBRANDT VAN RIJN: View on the Amstel, Near Kostverloren, with a Fence in the Foreground

90. REMBRANDT VAN RIJN:
Verso: Bust of a Bearded Man in Profile, in a High Cap

93. REMBRANDT VAN RIJN: Water-Meadows at Houtewael, Near the St. Anthonispoort

93. Verso. REMBRANDT VAN RIJN: Sketch of Cottages

94. REMBRANDT VAN RIJN: View on the Bullewijk, Looking Towards Ouderkerk, with a Rowing Boat

95. REMBRANDT VAN RIJN: A Village Inn by the Roadside

97. REMBRANDT VAN RIJN: View of Sloten

96. REMBRANDT VAN RIJN: Two Thatched Cottages

98. SIR PETER PAUL RUBENS: Sketches for a Wolf-Hunt

99. SIR PETER PAUL RUBENS: A Fallen Tree Lying by a Pool

100. SIR PETER PAUL RUBENS: Four Nude Female Figures Round a Basin

101. ROELANT SAVERY: A Dredger on a Wide River

102. BAVARIAN SCHOOL: A Battle by a Bridge Over a Wide River Issuing from a Lake

103. GERMAN (?) SCHOOL: An Old Man, Three-quarter Length, Gesticulating

104. SWISS SCHOOL, EXTENSIVELY REWORKED BY RUBENS: A Lady Holding a Shield: A Design for Glass

105a. HANS BALDUNG GRIEN (?): Sheet from a sketchbook, A Peasant Seated, and A House Among Trees in a Landscape

105b. HANS BALDUNG GRIEN (?): Sheet from a sketchbook, An Executioner

106. JÖRG BREU (The Younger): A Party in the Grounds of a Moated Castle

107. ALBRECHT DÜRER: The Virgin and Child with the Infant St. John

108. HANS ROTTENHAMMER: The Raising of Lazarus

109. JACQUES CALLOT: Louis de Lorraine-Guise, Prince de Phalsburg, on Horseback

110. JACQUES CALLOT: Landscape with Bathers

111a. JACQUES CALLOT: The Taking of Christ

111b. JACQUES CALLOT: Christ Before Pilate

112a. JACQUES CALLOT: Ecce Homo

112b. JACQUES CALLOT: Christ Crowned with Thorns

113a. JACQUES CALLOT: The Procession to Calvary

113b. JACQUES CALLOT: Christ Nailed to the Cross

114a. JACQUES CALLOT: Calvary

114b. JACQUES CALLOT: The Descent from the Cross

114c. JACQUES CALLOT: The Resurrection

115a. JACQUES CALLOT:
A Woman Holding a Spindle

115b. JACQUES CALLOT:
A Woman with a Basket on Her Arm

116. CLAUDE GELLÉE, called LE LORRAIN: St. John the Baptist Preaching in a Rocky Landscape

117. CLAUDE GELLÉE, called LE LORRAIN: Landscape with Christ Preaching The Sermon on the Mount

118. CLAUDE GELLÉE, called LE LORRAIN: Wooded Landscape with Jupiter and Callisto

119. NICOLAS POUSSIN: Apollo and Daphne

120. NICOLAS POUSSIN: The Rape of the Sabines